THE KEY

STUDENT STUDY GUIDE

Physics 20

THE KEY student study guide is designed to help students achieve success in school. The content in each study guide is 100% curriculum aligned and serves as an excellent source of material for review and practice. To create this book, teachers, curriculum specialists, and assessment experts have worked closely to develop the instructional pieces that explain each of the key concepts for the course. The practice questions and sample tests have detailed solutions that show problem-solving methods, highlight concepts that are likely to be tested, and point out potential sources of errors. **THE KEY** is a complete guide to be used by students throughout the school year for reviewing and understanding course content, and to prepare for assessments.

D1096476

Rao, Gautam, 1961 –

THE KEY – Physics 20 Alberta

1. Science – Juvenile Literature. I. Title

Published by
Castle Rock Research Corp.
2340 Manulife Place
10180 – 101 Street
Edmonton, AB T5J 3S4

14 15 16 FP 13 12 11

Publisher
Gautam Rao

Contributors
Barry Edgar
Phil Jones
Karen Kline
Kevin Okamura
Aaron Stavne
Del Taylor
Hans Van Kessel

Dedicated to the memory of Dr. V. S. Rao

THE KEY—Physics 20

THE KEY consists of the following sections:

KEY Tips for Being Successful at School gives examples of study and review strategies. It includes information about learning styles, study schedules, and note taking for test preparation.

Class Focus includes a unit on each area of the curriculum. Units are divided into sections, each focusing on one of the specific expectations, or main ideas, that students must learn about in that unit. Examples, definitions, and visuals help to explain each main idea. Practice questions on the main ideas are also included. At the end of each unit is a test on the important ideas covered. The practice questions and unit tests help students identify areas they know and those they need to study more. They can also be used as preparation for tests and quizzes. Most questions are of average difficulty, though some are easy and some are hard—the harder questions are called *Challenger Questions*. Each unit is prefaced by a **Table of Correlations**, which correlates questions in the unit to the specific curriculum expectations. Answers and solutions are found at the end of each unit.

KEY Strategies for Success on Tests helps students get ready for tests. It shows students different types of questions they might see, word clues to look for when reading them, and hints for answering them.

Practice Tests includes one to three tests based on the entire course. They are very similar to the format and level of difficulty that students may encounter on final tests. In some regions, these tests may be reprinted versions of official tests, or reflect the same difficulty levels and formats as official versions. This gives students the chance to practice using real-world examples. Answers and complete solutions are provided at the end of the section.

For the complete curriculum document (including specific expectations along with examples and sample problems), visit http://education.alberta.ca/teachers/program/science/programs.aspx.

THE KEY *Study Guides* are available for many courses. Check www.castlerockresearch.com for a complete listing of books available for your area.

For information about any of our resources or services, please call Castle Rock Research at 780.448.9619 or visit our website at http://www.castlerockresearch.com.

At Castle Rock Research, we strive to produce an error-free resource. If you should find an error, please contact us so that future editions can be corrected.

TABLE OF CONTENTS

KEY Tips for Being Successful at School

KEY TIPS FOR BEING SUCCESSFUL AT SCHOOL

KEY FACTORS CONTRIBUTING TO SCHOOL SUCCESS

In addition to learning the content of your courses, there are some other things that you can do to help you do your best at school. Some of these strategies are listed below.

- **Keep a positive attitude:** Always reflect on what you can already do and what you already know.

- **Be prepared to learn**: Have ready the necessary pencils, pens, notebooks, and other required materials for participating in class.

- **Complete all of your assignments:** Do your best to finish all of your assignments. Even if you know the material well, practice will reinforce your knowledge. If an assignment or question is difficult for you, work through it as far as you can so that your teacher can see exactly where you are having difficulty.

- **Set small goals for yourself when you are learning new material:** For example, when learning the parts of speech, do not try to learn everything in one night. Work on only one part or section each study session. When you have memorized one particular part of speech and understand it, then move on to another one, continue this process until you have memorized and learned all the parts of speech.

- **Review your classroom work regularly at home:** Review to be sure that you understand the material that you learned in class.

- **Ask your teacher for help**: Your teacher will help you if you do not understand something or if you are having a difficult time completing your assignments.

- **Get plenty of rest and exercise:** Concentrating in class is hard work. It is important to be well-rested and have time to relax and socialize with your friends. This helps you to keep your positive attitude about your school work.

- **Eat healthy meals:** A balanced diet keeps you healthy and gives you the energy that you need for studying at school and at home.

How To Find Your Learning Style

Every student learns differently. The manner in which you learn best is called your learning style. By knowing your learning style, you can increase your success at school. Most students use a combination of learning styles. Do you know what type of learner you are? Read the following descriptions. Which of these common learning styles do you use most often?

- **Linguistic Learner**: You may learn best by saying, hearing, and seeing words. You are probably really good at memorizing things such as dates, places, names, and facts. You may need **to write and then say out loud** the steps in a process, a formula, or the actions that lead up to a significant event.

- **Spatial Learner**: You may learn best by looking at and working with pictures. You are probably really good at puzzles, imagining things, and reading maps and charts. You may need to use strategies like **mind mapping and webbing** to organize your information and study notes.

- **Kinaesthetic Learner**: You may learn best by touching, moving, and figuring things out using manipulative. You are probably really good at physical activities and learning through movement. You may need to **draw your finger over a diagram** to remember it, **"tap out" the steps** needed to solve a problem, or **"feel" yourself writing or typing** a formula.

SCHEDULING STUDY TIME

You should review your class notes regularly to ensure that you have a clear understanding of all the new material you learned. Reviewing your lessons on a regular basis helps you to learn and remember ideas and concepts. It also reduces the quantity of material that you need to study prior to a test. Establishing a study schedule will help you to make the best use of your time.

Regardless of the type of study schedule you use, you may want to consider the following suggestions to maximize your study time and effort:

- Organize your work so that you begin with the most challenging material first.
- Divide the subject's content into small, manageable chunks.
- Alternate regularly between your different subjects and types of study activities in order to maintain your interest and motivation.
- Make a daily list with headings like "Must Do," "Should Do," and "Could Do."
- Begin each study session by quickly reviewing what you studied the day before.
- Maintain your usual routine of eating, sleeping, and exercising to help you concentrate better for extended periods of time.

CREATING STUDY NOTES

MIND-MAPPING OR WEBBING

Use the key words, ideas, or concepts from your reading or class notes to create a *mind map* or *web* (a diagram or visual representation of the given information). A mind map or web is sometimes referred to as a knowledge map.

- Write the key word, concept, theory, or formula in the centre of your page.

- Write down related facts, ideas, events, and information and then link them to the central concept with lines.

- Use coloured markers, underlining, or other symbols to emphasize things such as relationships, time lines, and important information.

- The following examples of a Frayer Model illustrate how this technique can be used to study scientific vocabulary.

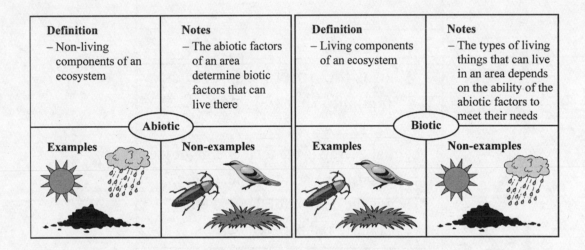

- On the reverse side, write the definition of the word, answer to the question, or any other important information that you want to remember.

> What is the difference between heat and thermal energy?

> What is the difference between heat and thermal energy?
>
> Thermal energy is the total energy of the particles in a solid, liquid, or gas. Heat is the amount of thermal energy transferred between objects.

SYMBOLS AND STICKY NOTES—IDENTIFYING IMPORTANT INFORMATION

Use symbols to mark your class notes. For example, an exclamation mark (!) might be used to point out something that must be learned well because it is a very important idea. A question mark (?) may highlight something that you are not certain about, and a diamond (◊) or asterisk (*) could highlight interesting information that you want to remember.

- Use sticky notes when you are not allowed to put marks in books.
- Use sticky notes to mark a page in a book that contains an important diagram, formula, explanation, etc.
- Use sticky notes to mark important facts in research books.

Key Tips 6 Castle Rock Research

MEMORIZATION TECHNIQUES

- **Association** relates new learning to something you already know. For example, to remember the spelling difference between *dessert* and *desert*, recall that the word *sand* has only one *s*. So, because there is sand in a desert, the word *desert* only has on *s*.

- **Mnemonic** devices are sentences that you create to remember a list or group of items. For example, the first letter of each word in the phrase "**E**very **G**ood **B**oy **D**eserves **F**udge" helps you to remember the names of the lines on the treble clef staff (E, G, B, D, and F) in music.

- **Acronyms** are words that are formed from the first letters or parts of the words in a group. For example, **RADAR** is actually an acronym for **Ra**dio **D**etecting **A**nd **R**anging, and **MASH** is an acronym for **M**obile **A**rmy **S**urgical **H**ospital. **HOMES** helps you to remember the names of the five Great Lakes (**H**uron, **O**ntario, **M**ichigan, **E**rie, and **S**uperior).

- **Visualizing** requires you to use your mind's eye to "see" a chart, list, map, diagram, or sentence as it is in your textbook or notes, on the chalk board or computer screen, or in a display.

- **Initialisms** are abbreviations that are formed from the first letters or parts of the words in a group. Unlike acronyms, initialisms cannot be pronounced as a word themselves. For example, **BEDMAS** is an initialism for the order of operations in math (**B**rackets, **E**xponents, **D**ivide, **M**ultiply, **A**dd, **S**ubtract).

KEY STRATEGIES FOR REVIEWING

Reviewing textbook material, class notes, and handouts should be an ongoing activity. Spending time reviewing becomes more critical when you are preparing for tests. You may find some of the following review strategies useful when studying during your scheduled study time.

- Before reading a selection, preview it by noting the headings, charts, graphs, and chapter questions.
- Before reviewing a unit, note the headings, charts, graphs and chapter questions.
- Highlight key concepts, vocabulary, definitions and formulas.
- Skim the paragraph and note the key words, phrases, and information.
- Carefully read over each step in a procedure.
- Draw a picture or diagram to help make the concept clearer.

KEY STRATEGIES FOR SUCCESS: A CHECKLIST

Review, review, review: review is a huge part of doing well at school and preparing for tests. Here is a checklist for you to keep track of how many suggested strategies for success you are using. Read each question and then put a check mark (✓) in the correct column. Look at the questions where you have checked the "No" column. Think about how you might try using some of these strategies to help you do your best at school.

KEY Strategies for Success	Yes	No
Do you attend school regularly?		
Do you know your personal learning style—how you learn best?		
Do you spend 15 to 30 minutes a day reviewing your notes?		
Do you study in a quiet place at home?		
Do you clearly mark the most important ideas in your study notes?		
Do you use sticky notes to mark texts and research books?		
Do you practise answering multiple-choice and written-response questions?		
Do you ask your teacher for help when you need it?		
Are you maintaining a healthy diet and sleep routine?		
Are you participating in regular physical activity?		

KINEMATICS

Table of Correlations				
Specific Expectation	**Practice Questions**	**Unit Test Questions**	**Practice Test 1**	**Practice Test 2**
Students will:				
A1 Describe motion in terms of displacement, velocity, acceleration, and time.				
A1.1 define, qualitatively and quantitatively, displacement, velocity, and acceleration	3, 5, 6, 7, NR1, 13, 15, 19	2, 3, 5, 10, NR4	2, 3, NR1, 5, NR2, 6, 10	2, 6, WR2
A1.2 define, operationally, and compare and contrast scalar and vector quantities	1, 4, 8, 9, 10,	1, 6, 7	1, 8	1
A1.3 explain, qualitatively and quantitatively, uniform and uniformly accelerated motion when provided with written descriptions and numerical and graphical data	2, NR2, 11, 12, 14, 16, NR3, 18, WR1	4, NR1, 8, NR2	4, 9	NR1, 3, NR2, 4, 5
A1.4 interpret, quantitatively, the motion of one object relative to another, using displacement and velocity vectors	17, NR5, NR6, 20, NR7, NR8	9	7	
A1.5 explain, quantitatively, two-dimensional motion in a horizontal or vertical plane, using vector components	NR4, 21, 22, 23	NR3, 11, 12		NR3, 7, NR4

KINEMATICS

A1.1 define, qualitatively and quantitatively, displacement, velocity and acceleration

A1.2 define, operationally, and compare and contrast scalar and vector quantities

THE PHYSICS OF MOTION

The position of an object is described by its location relative to some reference point. Displacement is the change of position of an object taken in a straight line, including the direction. Distance is the length of the path actually taken, and it does not include direction.

Vector quantities have both magnitude (size) and direction. Scalar quantities have only magnitude. Distance is a scalar quantity, while displacement is a vector quantity.

Speed and velocity both describe movement. They describe the amount of change in an object's position during a time interval. Speed has no direction and is found by dividing the distance by the time taken. It is a scalar quantity. Velocity, on the other hand, is found by dividing the displacement by the time taken. It has a direction (equal to the displacement's direction). It is a vector quantity.

Acceleration is another vector quantity describing motion. It describes a rate of change in velocity. Acceleration is the amount of velocity change over a specific time interval. Velocity and acceleration can be constant or variable. A constant velocity or acceleration changes by the same amount each second. A variable velocity or acceleration involves changes that vary in different time intervals.

Example

One city is southeast of another. A car drives 280 km between the airports of the two cities while a plane completes the trip by flying only 250 km SE.

This tells us that the distance between the cities on the roads is 280 km while the displacement from the first to the second city is 250 km SE.

Example

A person walks 20 m east, then 30 m west. His displacement is 10 m west since that is the single straight line change of position from the start of his two motions. His distance travelled is 50 m.

Example

A car drives 10 km north in 20 minutes.

Its speed and velocity have the same magnitude (10 km / 20 min = 0.50 km/min) since there was no change of direction. The velocity includes the direction north.

Example

A bicycle speeds up from 2.0 m/s east to 8.0 m/s east in 3.0 s.

Its acceleration is found by dividing the change of velocity (6.0 m/s east) by the time (3.0 s) and is equal to 2.0 m/s^2 east.

Practice Questions: 1, 3, 4, NR1, 5, 6, 7, 8, 9, 10, 13, 15, 19

A1.3 explain, qualitatively and quantitatively, uniform and uniformly accelerated motion when provided with written descriptions and numerical and graphical data

ACCELERATED MOTION

Information can be given in graphical or algebraic form.

GRAPHICALLY

A graph that represents something as a function of time (time is on the horizontal axis) has a slope that measures a rate of change. This means that:

- The slope of a distance-time graph is equal to the speed of the object whose motion is graphed

- The slope of a displacement-time graph is equal to the velocity of the object

- The slope of a velocity-time graph is equal to the acceleration of the object

Example

In a distance-time graph, as shown in Fig. 1, the slope indicates speed. In a displacement-time graph, the slope indicates velocity.

Fig. 1

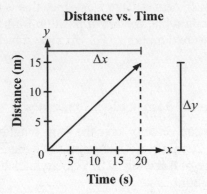

$$\text{Slope} = \frac{\Delta y}{\Delta x} \quad (\text{units})$$
$$= \frac{m}{s}$$

Example

In a velocity-time graph, as shown in Fig. 2, the slope indicates acceleration.

Fig. 2

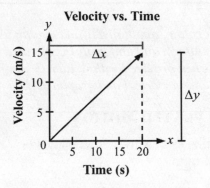

$$\text{Slope} = \frac{\Delta y}{\Delta x} \quad (\text{units})$$
$$= \frac{\frac{m}{s}}{s}$$
$$= \frac{m}{s^2}$$

The area under the curve for these graphs is the area between the line (or curve) and the horizontal (time) axis and between two times. Multiplying the average value of the *y*-axis variable by the time over which it is applied is one way to determine the area under the curve.

The area under an acceleration-time graph equals the change of velocity of the object whose motion is graphed.

The area under a velocity-time graph equals the change of position of the object. This is the displacement of the object.

Example

The area under the curve in Fig. 3 shows you the distance travelled by the object relative to its starting position, or its displacement.

Fig. 3

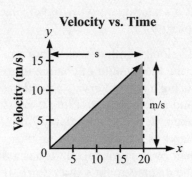

$$\text{Area} = \frac{1}{2} \text{ height} \times \text{base} \quad (\text{units})$$
$$= s \times \frac{m}{s}$$
$$= m$$

Example

The area under the curve in Fig. 4 shows you the change in velocity of the object.

Fig. 4

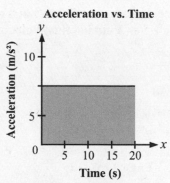

Acceleration vs. Time

$$\text{Area} = \text{length} \times \text{width} \quad \text{(units)}$$
$$= \frac{m}{s^2} \times s$$
$$= \frac{m}{s}$$

Uniform motion is a consistent change of position in one direction.

Example

In Fig. 5, you are consistently changing displacement in one direction as shown by the single slope. This is called uniform velocity.

Fig. 5

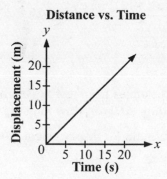

Distance vs. Time

Example

In Fig. 6, you have consistently changing velocity in one direction. Again, this is evident in the single slope. This is called uniform acceleration.

Fig. 6

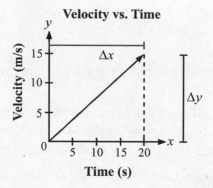

Velocity vs. Time

ALGEBRAICALLY

For uniform motion, divide the displacement by the time to get the velocity (or speed if direction is unimportant).

$$\vec{v} = \frac{\Delta \vec{d}}{\Delta t}$$

The arrows on the symbols indicate the vector nature of the quantities. It also indicates that the direction of the velocity is the same as the direction of the displacement. The delta (Δ) means that both the displacement and time are intervals.

Example

A wagon travels 45 m in 9.0 s. What is its speed? (Because no direction is specified, speed is a valid variable.)

$$v = \frac{d}{t}$$
$$= \frac{45 \text{ m}}{9.0 \text{ s}}$$
$$= 5.0 \text{ m/s}$$

Often, the delta symbol is omitted for the variables of displacement and time. This is acceptable as long as you understand you are still working with intervals.

Example

How far will a car go if it travels at 100 km/h for 2.50 h?

$$v = \frac{d}{t}$$
$$\Rightarrow d = vt$$
$$= 100 \text{ km/h} \times 2.50 \text{ h}$$
$$= 250 \text{ km}$$

Therefore, the distance travelled by the car is 250 km

Things get more complicated when objects accelerate. You now have to keep track of an initial velocity $(\vec{v}_i)$, a final velocity $(\vec{v}_f)$, the rate of acceleration $(\vec{a})$, the displacement $(\vec{d})$, and the time (t).

Acceleration is defined as the rate of change of velocity.

$$\vec{a} = \frac{\vec{v}_f - \vec{v}_i}{\Delta t}$$

Example

A car accelerates from 5.0 m/s to 15.0 m/s in 2.0 s. Find its acceleration.

$$\vec{a} = \frac{\vec{v}_f - \vec{v}_i}{t}$$
$$= \frac{15 \text{ m/s} - 5.0 \text{ m/s}}{2.0 \text{ s}}$$
$$= +5.0 \text{ m/s}^2$$

Example

A cyclist is moving at 10.0 m/s when she puts on the brakes and slows to 1.0 m/s over a time of 3.0 s. Her acceleration is

$$\vec{a} = \frac{\vec{v}_f - \vec{v}_i}{t}$$
$$= \frac{1.0 \text{ m/s} - 10.0 \text{ m/s}}{3.0 \text{ s}}$$
$$= -3.0 \text{ m/s}^2$$

The negative answer here means that the acceleration is in the opposite direction as the initial velocity. The initial velocity is taken to be positive, so the bike is slowing down in this case.

A negative acceleration can also mean speeding up in a negative direction, and a positive acceleration can be slowing down in a negative direction.

Example

A runner accelerates from 2.0 m/s at a rate of 4.0 m/s² for 1.5 s. Find his final velocity.

$$\vec{a} = \frac{\vec{v}_f - \vec{v}_i}{t}$$
$$\Rightarrow \vec{v}_f = \vec{v}_i + \vec{a}t$$
$$= 2.0 \text{ m/s} + (4.0 \text{ m/s}^2)(1.5 \text{ s})$$
$$= +8.0 \text{ m/s}$$

AVERAGE VELOCITY

If something undergoes a uniform acceleration, its velocity-time graph is a straight line and the average velocity is the midpoint of the graph's line.

$$\vec{v}_{average} = \frac{\vec{v}_i + \vec{v}_f}{2} \text{ and } \vec{d} = \left(\frac{\vec{v}_i + \vec{v}_f}{2}\right)\Delta t$$

Example

A train accelerates from 2.00 m/s east to 18.0 m/s east in a time of 90.0 s. What is the displacement of the train?

$$\vec{d} = \left(\frac{\vec{v}_i + \vec{v}_f}{2}\right)\Delta t$$
$$= \left(\frac{2.00 \text{ m/s} + 18.0 \text{ m/s}}{2}\right) \times 90.0 \text{ s}$$
$$= 900 \text{ m east}$$

Example

A rocket accelerates from rest to 100 m/s upward while travelling 80.0 m. How long did this take?

Using the formula for displacement, you can solve for time taken:

$$\vec{d} = \left(\frac{\vec{v}_i + \vec{v}_f}{2}\right)t$$
$$\Rightarrow t = \frac{2\vec{d}}{(\vec{v}_i + \vec{v}_f)}$$
$$= \frac{2 \times 80.0 \text{ m}}{(0 + 100 \text{ m/s})}$$
$$= 1.60 \text{ s}$$

The rocket takes 1.60 s to travel the given distance.

Finally, these two equations for velocity and displacement can be combined to produce three more equations:

$$\vec{d} = \vec{v}_i t + \frac{1}{2} \vec{a} t^2$$

$$\vec{d} = \vec{v}_f t - \frac{1}{2} \vec{a} t^2$$

$$v_f^2 = v_i^2 + 2ad$$

Each equation is useful, depending upon the information given.

Example

A ball accelerates from 4.0 m/s west at a rate of 6.0 m/s² while travelling 5.0 m west across a room. Find its final velocity.

$$\begin{aligned} v_f^2 &= v_i^2 + 2ad \\ &= \left(4.0 \text{ m/s}\right)^2 + 2 \times 6.0 \text{ m/s}^2 \times 5.0 \text{ m} \\ \therefore v_f &= \sqrt{76 \text{ m}^2/\text{s}^2} \\ &= 8.7 \text{ m/s} \end{aligned}$$

The final velocity of the ball is 8.7 m/s west.

Example

A bullet is fired out of a gun at 400 m/s. If the barrel of the gun is 0.800 m long, then find the magnitude of acceleration of the bullet as it moved from rest to the end of the barrel.

$$\begin{aligned} v_f^2 &= v_i^2 + 2ad \\ \Rightarrow a &= \frac{v_f^2 - v_i^2}{2d} \\ &= \frac{\left(400 \text{ m/s}\right)^2 - 0^2}{2 \times 0.800 \text{ m}} \\ &= 1.00 \times 10^5 \text{ m/s}^2 \end{aligned}$$

Example

A brick falls from rest and accelerates downward at 9.81 m/s² for 1.50 s. How far does it fall?

$$\begin{aligned} \vec{d} &= \vec{v}_i t + \frac{1}{2} \vec{a} t^2 \\ &= 0 \times 1.50 \text{ s} + \frac{1}{2} \times 9.81 \text{ m/s}^2 \times \left(1.50 \text{ s}\right)^2 \\ &= 11.0 \text{ m down} \end{aligned}$$

Example

A car travelling at 20 m/s south slows down over a time of 3.0 s while travelling 50 m south. Find the car's acceleration.

$$\begin{aligned} \vec{d} &= \vec{v}_i t + \frac{1}{2} \vec{a} t^2 \\ \Rightarrow \vec{a} &= \frac{2\left(\vec{d} - \vec{v}_i t\right)}{t^2} \\ &= \frac{2\left(50 \text{ m} - 20 \text{ m/s} \times 3.0 \text{ s}\right)}{\left(3.0 \text{ s}\right)^2} \\ &= -2.2 \text{ m/s}^2 \end{aligned}$$

Note that the negative acceleration means the car is slowing down.

Example

A bus brakes to a stop, decelerating at 7.00 m/s² for 2.00 s. How far does it go during this time?

$$\begin{aligned} \vec{d} &= \vec{v}_f t - \frac{1}{2} \vec{a} t^2 \\ &= 0 \times 2.00 \text{ s} - \frac{1}{2}\left(-7.00 \text{ m/s}^2\right) \times \left(2.00 \text{ s}\right)^2 \\ &= 14.0 \text{ m forward} \end{aligned}$$

Practice Questions: 2, NR2, 11, 12, 14, 16, NR3, 18, WR1

A1.4   interpret, quantitatively, the motion of one object relative to another, using displacement and velocity vectors

VECTORS: DISPLACEMENT AND VELOCITY

When an object undergoes two displacements, you can find the total displacement by placing the second displacement after the first one.

The way to add two vectors is to place them "tip to tail." The resultant vector is the straight line vector from the start of the first vector to the end of the second one.

Example

A cart travels 20 m east and 20 m north. Find the total displacement.

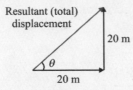

Use the Pythagorean theorem to find the magnitude of the resultant displacement, and trigonometry to find its direction.

$$d_R = \sqrt{(20\ m)^2 + (20\ m)^2}$$
$$= 28\ m$$

$$\theta = \tan^{-1}\frac{20\ m}{20\ m}$$
$$= 45°$$

The cart's displacement is 28 m 45° NE.

This makes it necessary to find a way to express angles.

The angles will be expressed as a number of degrees from one of the four cardinal points of a compass (north, south, east, and west) and toward another cardinal point.

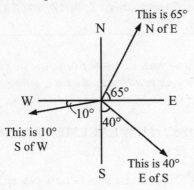

If the vectors are in the same line, the resultant can be found by adding or subtracting their magnitudes.

Example

A person walks 2.0 m east, 3.0 m east, and 6.0 m west. Find her total displacement.

Place the vectors tip to tail.

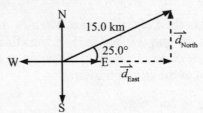

$$\vec{d} = 2.0\ m + 3.0\ m - 6.0\ m$$
$$= -1.0\ m$$

The displacement is –1.0 m east or 1.0 m west.

If you get a non-right angle triangle when you add the vectors, then finding the resultant direction is a bit complicated. You can use the laws of sines and cosines, or you can use perpendicular components. These are two vectors that are perpendicular to each other that add up to each of the original vectors.

Example

A bike moves 15.0 km at 25.0° N of E. Find the northward and eastward components of this displacement vector.

Each component of $\vec{d}$ can be found using trigonometry. The original vector is always the hypotenuse, and the component vectors are either the side adjacent or opposite the labelled angle.

$$d_x \text{ (eastward component)} = (15.0\ km)\cos 25.0°$$
$$= 13.6\ km$$
$$d_y \text{ (northward component)} = (15.0\ km)\sin 25.0°$$
$$= 6.34\ km$$

If you travelled 13.6 km east and then 6.34 km north, you would be in the same place as if you went 15.0 km 25.0° N of E.

To add two vectors, break each one into its *x*- and *y*-components, add the components, and combine the sums of the components.

Example

From point P, a man walks 500 m 30.0° north of east and reaches a point Q. He then walks 60.0° north of east for 700 m. How far away, and in what direction, is the man from point P?

Find the magnitude of the components of the first displacement vector $(\vec{d})$.

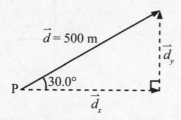

Consider east and north to be positive.

$$d_y = d\sin\theta$$
$$= (500 \text{ m})\sin 30.0°$$
$$= 250.0 \text{ m}$$
$$d_x = d\cos\theta$$
$$= (500 \text{ m})\cos 30.0°$$
$$= 433.0 \text{ m}$$

Find the magnitude of the components of the other vector $(\vec{d}')$.

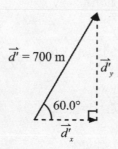

$$d'_y = d'\sin\theta$$
$$= (700 \text{ m})\sin 60.0°$$
$$= 606.2 \text{ m}$$
$$d'_x = d'\cos\theta$$
$$= (700 \text{ m})\cos 60.0°$$
$$= 350.0 \text{ m}$$

Add the horizontal components.

$$d_{xR} = d_x + d'_x$$
$$= 433.0 \text{ m} + 350.0 \text{ m}$$
$$= 783.0 \text{ m}$$

Add the vertical components.

$$d_{yR} = d_y + d'_y$$
$$= 250.0 \text{ m} + 606.2 \text{ m}$$
$$= 856.2 \text{ m}$$

Put the totals together. They always make a right triangle.

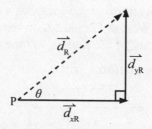

The magnitude of the resultant displacement is

$$d_R = \sqrt{(783.0 \text{ m})^2 + (856.2 \text{ m})^2}$$
$$= 1\,160.2 \text{ m}$$
$$= 1.16 \times 10^3 \text{ m}$$

Now, find the direction of the resultant displacement using the tangent function.

$$\tan\theta = \frac{856.2 \text{ m}}{783.0 \text{ m}}$$
$$\therefore \theta = 47.6° \text{ north of east}$$

The displacement is 1.16 km 47.6° N of E.

Another legitimate way to add vectors is to place them tip to tail in an accurate scale diagram. You can then use a ruler and protractor to draw the vectors and measure the resultant. Here is a scale drawing for the previous example question.

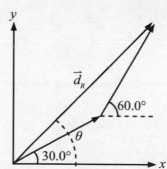

Velocity vectors are handled the same way as displacement vectors. All motion is measured relative to (**w**ith **r**espect **t**o or *wrt*) some reference frame. If you walk on a moving boat, your velocity relative to the boat is different from your velocity relative to the water.

In general, if something is moving on a moving platform, the velocity of that something *wrt* the ground is equal to its velocity *wrt* the moving platform plus the velocity of the platform *wrt* the ground.

Example

A person walks north at 3.5 km/h on a cruise ship that is sailing west at 12.5 km/h on the ocean. Find the velocity of the person *wrt* the ocean.

The ship is the platform, so:

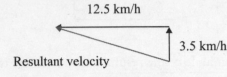

12.5 km/h

3.5 km/h

Resultant velocity

$$v = \sqrt{(3.5 \text{ km/h})^2 + (12.5 \text{ km/h})^2}$$
$$= 13 \text{ km/h}$$

at an angle $\theta = \tan^{-1} \dfrac{12.5 \text{ km/h}}{3.5 \text{ km/h}}$
$$= 74° \text{ W of N}$$

The velocity is 13 km/h 74° W of N. (This is the same direction as 16° N of W).

Again, if the vectors produce an oblique triangle:

1. Resolve into components $\vec{v}_x$ and $\vec{v}_y$, and $\vec{v}_x'$ and $\vec{v}_y'$

2. Add components
$$\vec{v} + \vec{v}' = (\vec{v}_x + \vec{v}_x') + (\vec{v}_y + \vec{v}_y')$$
$$= \vec{v}_x + \vec{v}_x' + \vec{v}_y + \vec{v}_y'$$

3. The resultant vector is $\vec{v}_R = \vec{v}_{xR} + \vec{v}_{yR}$

4. The direction is found using $\tan \theta = \dfrac{v_{yR}}{v_{xR}}$

5. The magnitude of the vector is
$$v_R = \sqrt{(v_{xR})^2 + (v_{yR})^2}$$

Example

A plane travelling 50.0° north of west *wrt* the air at 225 km/h experiences a 50.0 km/h wind blowing 15.0° south of west. What is the plane's resultant velocity *wrt* the ground?

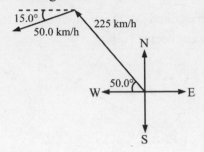

Solution (algebraic)

Consider west and north to be positive. The magnitudes of the components of the velocity vectors are as follows:

Plane:
$$v_x = (225 \text{ km/h}) \cos 50.0°$$
$$= 145 \text{ km/h}$$
$$\therefore \vec{v}_x = 145 \text{ km/h west}$$
$$v_y = (225 \text{ km/h}) \sin 50.0°$$
$$= 172 \text{ km/h}$$
$$\therefore \vec{v}_y = 172 \text{ km/h north}$$

Wind:
$$v_x = (50.0 \text{ km/h}) \cos(15.0°)$$
$$= 48.3 \text{ km/h}$$
$$\therefore \vec{v}_x = 48.3 \text{ km/h west}$$
$$v_y = (50.0 \text{ km/h}) \sin(15.0°)$$
$$= 12.9 \text{ km/h}$$
$$\therefore \vec{v}_y = 12.9 \text{ km/h south}$$

Add the components of the vectors to get the component velocity vectors along the west and north directions.
$$\vec{v}_{xR} = 145 \text{ km/h} + 48.3 \text{ km/h}$$
$$= 193 \text{ km/h west}$$
$$\vec{v}_{yR} = 172 \text{ km/h} - 12.9 \text{ km/h}$$
$$= 159 \text{ km/h north}$$

Use the Pythagorean theorem to find the magnitude of the resultant velocity of the plane.
$$v_R = \sqrt{v_{xR}^2 + v_{yR}^2}$$
$$= \sqrt{(193 \text{ km/h})^2 + (159 \text{ km/h})^2}$$
$$= 250 \text{ km/h}$$

Now, find the direction of the resultant velocity using the tangent function.

$$\tan \theta = \frac{v_y}{v_x}$$

$$= \frac{159 \text{ km/h}}{193 \text{ km/h}}$$

$$\therefore \theta = \tan^{-1}\left(\frac{159 \text{ km/h}}{193 \text{ km/h}}\right)$$

$$= 39.5° \text{ north of west}$$

The velocity of the plane is 250 km/h at 39.5° N of W *wrt* the ground.

Solution (graphical)

Draw the vectors to scale, placing the tail of the second vector onto the head of the first vector. Draw the resultant vector from the tail of the first vector to the tip of the second one. Measure using a ruler and use the scale to calculate the final velocity. To find the direction, use a protractor, measuring from the appropriate axis.

Example

A plane travelling at a velocity of 225 km/h, 55° north of east *wrt* the air experiences a 75 km/h wind blowing 35° south of east. How long will it take for the plane to travel between two cities 400 km apart along its resultant path?

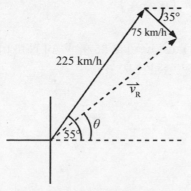

For this problem, consider east and north to be positive. Then the magnitudes of the components of the velocity are as follows:

Plane:

$$v_x = (225 \text{ km/h})\cos 55°$$

$$= +129 \text{ km/h}$$

$$\therefore \vec{v}_x = 129 \text{ km/h east}$$

$$v_y = (225 \text{ km/h})\sin 55°$$

$$= +184 \text{ km/h}$$

$$\therefore \vec{v}_y = 184 \text{ km/h north}$$

Wind:

$$v_x = (75 \text{ km/h})\cos(35°)$$

$$= +61.4 \text{ km/h}$$

$$\therefore \vec{v}_x = 61.4 \text{ km/h east}$$

$$v_y = (75 \text{ km/h})\sin(35°)$$

$$= 43.0 \text{ km/h}$$

$$\therefore \vec{v}_y = 43.0 \text{ km/h south}$$

Next, add the components of the vectors to get the resultant velocity vectors along east and north directions.

$$\vec{v}_{xR} = 129 \text{ km/h} + 61.4 \text{ km/h}$$

$$= +190.4 \text{ km/h}$$

$$\vec{v}_{yR} = 184 \text{ km/h} - 43.0 \text{ km/h}$$

$$= +141.0 \text{ km/h}$$

Use the Pythagorean theorem to find the magnitude of the resultant velocity of the plane.

$$v_R = \sqrt{v_{xR}^2 + v_{yR}^2}$$

$$= \sqrt{(190.4 \text{ km/h})^2 + (141.0 \text{ km/h})^2}$$

$$= 237 \text{ km/h}$$

Now, find the direction of the resultant velocity using the tangent function.

$$\tan \theta = \frac{v_{yR}}{v_{xR}}$$

$$= \frac{(141.0 \text{ km/h})}{(190.4 \text{ km/h})}$$

$$\theta = 36.5° \text{ north of east}$$

Use the magnitude of the velocity of the plane to find the time it took to travel between the two cities.

$$v = \frac{d}{t}$$

$$\Rightarrow t = \frac{d}{v}$$

$$= \frac{400 \text{ km}}{237 \text{ km/h}}$$

$$= 1.7 \text{ h}$$

It will take 1.7 h for the plane to travel between the two cities.

Example

A boat moves at 2.00 m/s over still water. It crosses a 50.0 m wide river flowing at 1.20 m/s east.

a) If the boat heads north, find its velocity *wrt* the ground.

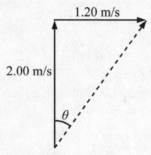

Add the velocities (tip to tail). The resultant is the velocity.

Use the Pythagorean theorem to find the magnitude of the resultant velocity.

$$v = \sqrt{(2.00 \text{ m/s})^2 + (1.20 \text{ m/s})^2}$$

$$= 2.33 \text{ m/s}$$

Now, find the direction of the resultant velocity using the tangent function.

$$\theta = \tan^{-1}\left(\frac{1.20 \text{ m/s}}{2.00 \text{ m/s}}\right)$$

$$= 31.0° \text{ E of N}$$

The velocity *wrt* the ground is 2.33 m/s 31.0° E of N.

b) How long will it take to cross the river?

The boat is crossing the river at 2.00 m/s speed, so the downstream drift does not affect how long the boat will take to cross the river. Use the 2.00 m/s to find how long it will take the boat to cross the river.

$$t = \frac{d}{v}$$

$$= \frac{50.0 \text{ m}}{2.00 \text{ m/s}}$$

$$= 25.0 \text{ s}$$

It will take 25.0 s to cross the river.

c) How far downstream will the boat drift while crossing the river?

The boat is drifting east at 1.20 m/s for the 25.0 s that it takes to cross the river. Use this velocity to find the eastward displacement.

$$\vec{d} = \vec{v}t$$

$$= 1.20 \text{ m/s} \times 25.0 \text{ s}$$

$$= 30.0 \text{ m east}$$

The boat drifts 30.0 m east while crossing.

d) With what angle must the boat move in order to actually go straight across the river?

Notice that this is a different triangle.
The resultant is **not** the hypotenuse of the triangle.

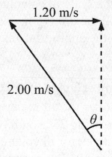

$$\theta = \sin^{-1}\left(\frac{1.20 \text{ m/s}}{2.00 \text{ m/s}}\right)$$

$$= 36.9°$$

The boat must head at 36.9° W of N to travel straight across the river.

e) How long will it take the boat to go straight across the river?

Use the Pythagorean theorem to find the magnitude of the resultant velocity.

$$v = \sqrt{(2.00 \text{ m/s})^2 - (1.20 \text{ m/s})^2}$$
$$= 1.60 \text{ m/s}$$

Use the resultant velocity to find how long it will take for the boat to cross the river.

$$t = \frac{d}{v}$$
$$= \frac{50.0 \text{ m}}{1.60 \text{ m/s}}$$
$$= 31.3 \text{ s}$$

It will take 31.3 s to go straight across the river (which makes sense since some of the boat's energy is spent fighting the current.)

Practice Questions: 17, NR5, NR6, 20, NR7, NR8

A1.5 *explain, quantitatively, two-dimensional motion in a horizontal or vertical plane, using vector components*

TWO-DIMENSIONAL MOTION

When things are thrown through the air at slow to moderate speeds, they make a parabolic arc through the air. The motion is a combination of a constant horizontal speed and a vertical acceleration of –9.81 m/s².

We can analyze a parabolic trajectory by handling the horizontal and vertical motions separately. The time in the air is the same for both components of the motion.

Example

A football is kicked from the ground at an angle of 35.0° with the horizontal at an initial velocity of 25.0 m/s. Find the following:

a) Initial Vertical and Horizontal Velocity

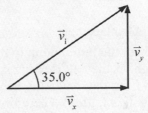

Vertical:
$$v_{iy} = v_i \sin 35.0°$$
$$= (25.0 \text{ m/s}) \sin 35.0°$$
$$= 14.3 \text{ m/s}$$
$$\therefore \vec{v}_{iy} = 14.3 \text{ m/s}$$

Horizontal:
$$v_{ix} = v_i \cos 35.0°$$
$$= (25.0 \text{ m/s}) \cos 35.0°$$
$$= 20.5 \text{ m/s}$$
$$\therefore \vec{v}_{ix} = 20.5 \text{ m/s}$$

b) Time of Flight

Vertical:
$$\vec{v}_{iy} = 14.3 \text{ m/s} \quad \text{(from previous calculation)}$$

$$\vec{a} = \vec{g}$$
$$= -9.81 \text{ m/s}^2 \quad \text{(acceleration due to gravity)}$$

$$\vec{v}_{y \text{ peak}} = 0 \quad \text{(when the football reaches its highest point)}$$

Therefore
$$\vec{v}_{y \text{ peak}} = \vec{v}_{iy} + \vec{a}t$$
$$0 = 14.3 \text{ m/s} + (-9.81 \text{ m/s}^2)(t)$$
$$14.3 \text{ m/s} = (9.81 \text{ m/s}^2)t$$
$$\Rightarrow t = 1.46 \text{ s}$$

This is the time it takes the ball to reach its peak from the ground. It represents half of the total flight of the ball.

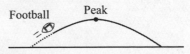

The total time of the flight is 2(1.46 s) = 2.92 s.

c) Maximum Height

$$d = \vec{v}_{iy}t + \frac{1}{2}\vec{a}t^2$$

$$= (14.3 \text{ m/s})(1.46 \text{ s}) + \frac{1}{2}(-9.81 \text{ m/s}^2) \times (1.46 \text{ s})^2$$

$$= 10.4 \text{ m}$$

d) Horizontal Displacement

The distance from the initial point to the maximum height as the ball is rising is the same as the distance from the maximum height to the ground as the ball is falling. Therefore, the vertical displacement is zero. The horizontal displacement is:

$$\vec{d}_x = \vec{v}_{ix}t$$

$$= (20.5 \text{ m/s})(2.92 \text{ s})$$

$$= 59.9 \text{ m}$$

The total displacement is the vertical displacement plus the horizontal displacement.

$d_t = d_v + d_h$

$= 0 \text{ m} + 59.9 \text{ m}$

$= 59.9 \text{ m}$

e) Horizontal Range

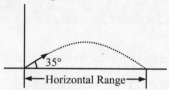

$$d_x = v_{ix}t$$

$$= (20.5 \text{ m/s})(2.92 \text{ s})$$

$$= 59.9 \text{ m}$$

The total range is 59.9 m

Example

Kyle, a stunt driver, wants to drive a motorcycle off a 4.0 m high parkade and into a lake. He needs a horizontal range of 13 m in order to land in water deep enough to keep him safe. With what speed must he leave the parkade?

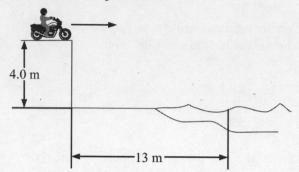

Time in the air: The initial vertical velocity is zero since he is moving horizontally.

$$\vec{d}_y = \vec{v}_{iy}t + \frac{1}{2}\vec{a}t^2$$

$$= 0 + \frac{1}{2}\vec{g}t^2$$

$$\Rightarrow t = \sqrt{\frac{2\vec{d}_y}{\vec{g}}}$$

$$= \sqrt{\frac{2(-4.0 \text{ m})}{-9.81 \text{ m/s}^2}}$$

$$= 0.903 \text{ s}$$

Find the speed needed to leave the parkade.

$$v_x = \frac{d_x}{t}$$

$$= \frac{13 \text{ m}}{0.903 \text{ s}}$$

$$= 14.4 \text{ m/s}$$

Since the rider needs to achieve at least 14.4 m/s, when rounding for significant digits, round it up instead of down. Thus, the stunt driver should leave the parkade at 15 m/s to be safe. If this were rounded down then the stunt rider would fall short of the water and not complete the stunt.

Practice Questions: NR4, 21, 22, 23

PRACTICE QUESTIONS—KINEMATICS

1. An example of a vector quantity is

   A. mass

   B. time

   C. length

   D. displacement

2. Assuming a parachute uniformly decelerates a skydiver, which of the following graphs **best** represents the motion of a skydiver after her parachute opens?

   A.

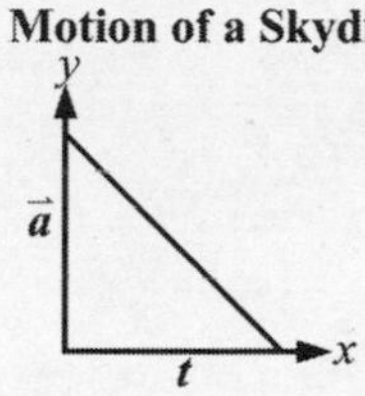

   B.

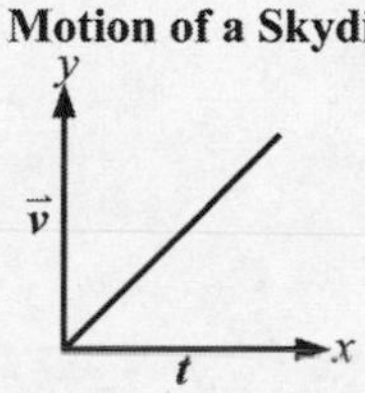

   C.

   D.

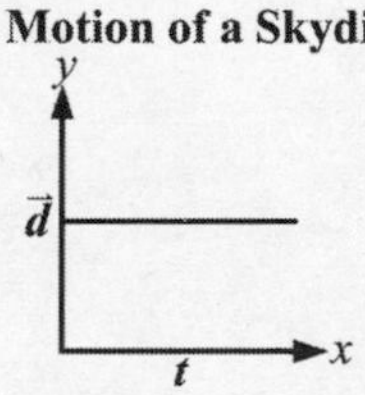

Use the following information to answer the next three questions.

The diagram below represents a multiple-flash photograph of a toy car moving forward across a horizontal table. The light was flashing at a rate of 10 flashes per second.

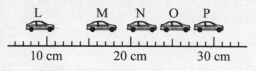

3. Which of the following statements is **not** a possible description of the motion of the car?

   A. The car was moving from left to right.

   B. The car was slowing down from position L to O.

   C. The car was travelling at a constant speed between M and O.

   D. The velocity of the car was constant between position N and P.

4. The car in the given diagram is travelling at its greatest speed between

   A. L and M

   B. M and N

   C. N and O

   D. O and P

Numerical Response

1. The average speed of the car in the diagram above, for the interval recorded was ____ cm/s.
(Round and record your answer to **two digits**.)

Use the following information to answer the next question.

The F-14 Tomcat fighter jet used in the US Navy is able to land on the small runway of an aircraft carrier because the plane's tailhook catches a wire on the carrier to slow the speed of the plane.

5. If the plane's velocity changes from 150 km/h to a stop in 2.00 s, what is the acceleration of the plane?

   A. −150 km/h^2

   B. −20.8 m/s^2

   C. 20.8 m/s^2

   D. 150 km/h^2

Use the following information to answer the next question.

One of the most rapid accelerations ever achieved was documented when driver Jankel Tempest took his vehicle from 0 to 96.0 km/h in 3.89 s.

6. Which of the following graphs describes this motion?

   A.
   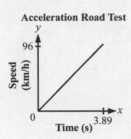

   B.
   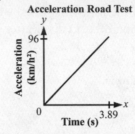

   C.
   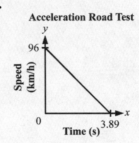

   D.
   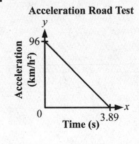

Use the following diagram to answer the next question.

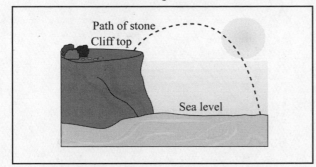

Path of stone
Cliff top
Sea level

7. A stone is thrown upward from a cliff top and follows a parabolic arc. Which of the following graphs shows the acceleration of the stone against time? (Note: neglect air resistance.)

A.

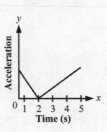

B.

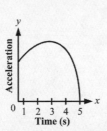

C.

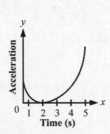

D.

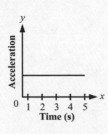

Use the following information to answer the next three questions.

The diagram represents a trolley being pulled along a frictionless table by a 100 g falling mass, causing the trolley to accelerate uniformly.

Prior to $t = 0$, the trolley is at rest. At $t = 0$, the weight begins to fall.

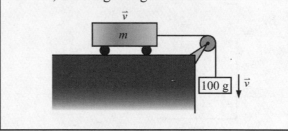

8. Which of the following graphs shows the correct distance versus time graph for the trolley?

A.

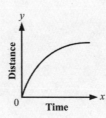

B.

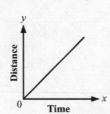

C.

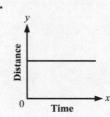

D.

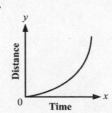

9. Which of the following graphs shows the correct velocity-time graph for the trolley?

A.

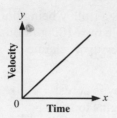

B.

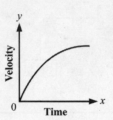

C.

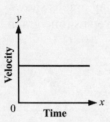

D.

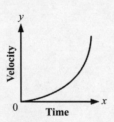

10. Which of the following graphs shows the correct acceleration-time graph for the trolley?

A.

B.

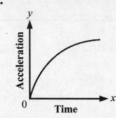

C.

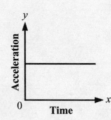

D.

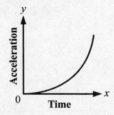

CHALLENGER QUESTION

Numerical Response

2. A typical modern supertanker is about 350 m long, and when fully loaded, travels at 8.50 m/s. It can take 5.00 km to bring this ship to a full stop. The time required to stop, expressed in scientific notation, is $a.bc \times 10^d$ s.

The value of *abcd* is _____.

11. Which of the following graphs shows an object undergoing uniformly accelerated motion?

A.

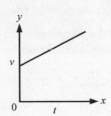

B.

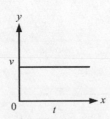

C.

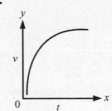

D.

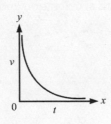

Use the following information to answer the next question.

On May 18, 1990, the French TGV high speed train set a world speed record at 515 km/h.

12. If the train started from rest and reached its maximum speed at 5.00 km, what is the magnitude of the train's average acceleration?

A. 1.33×10^4 km/h^2

B. 2.65×10^4 km/h^2

C. 5.31×10^4 km/h^2

D. 1.33×10^5 km/h^2

Use the following additional information to answer the next question.

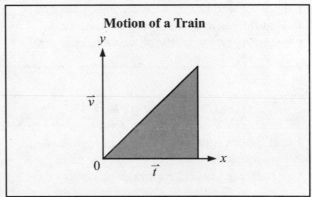

Motion of a Train

13. The shaded area represents

A. total time

B. acceleration

C. displacement

D. average velocity

CHALLENGER QUESTION

Numerical Response

3. A sonar impulse is transmitted vertically downward from a stationary boat, and the sonar impulse, reflected from the sea bed, is received on the boat after a 10.0 s interval. Assuming that the speed of sound in water is 1 450 m/s, the depth of the water under the boat, expressed in scientific notation, is $a.bc \times 10d$ m. The values of a, b, c, and d is _____. (Record your answer as a **four-digit** number.)

Use the following information to answer the next two questions.

A new feature at the Olympic Games is the "dive camera" that tapes a diver's progress from the platform to under the water. The camera falls at the same free fall rate as the diver. (Assume initial velocity of the camera is zero.)

CHALLENGER QUESTION

14. If the dive platform is 10.0 m high, how many complete dives can be recorded on a 30.0 min tape, if the camera films from the start of the dive until 1.00 s of underwater time for each dive and if there is a 1.00 s interval of blank tape between each dive? (A complete dive consists of the dive, the underwater recording, and the one second blank space.)

   A. 100

   B. 280

   C. 524

   D. 704

Use the following information to answer the next question.

When something falls through the air, after a certain amount of time, it reaches what is called  "terminal velocity." At this velocity, there is no longer any acceleration, and the object falls at a constant speed. This occurs because the force due to air resistance at this speed equals, and opposes, the gravitational force on the object. When skydivers jump out of an airplane, they initially accelerate toward Earth at 9.81 m/s². Suppose that the terminal velocity of skydiver Brian Heath is 55.6 m/s. When his parachute opens, it provides a deceleration of 30 m/s².

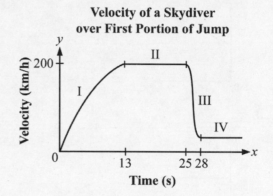

Velocity of a Skydiver over First Portion of Jump

15. On the previous graph, phases I and II represent, respectively,

   A. terminal velocity and hitting an updraft

   B. terminal velocity and the parachute opening

   C. falling at a constant acceleration and the parachute opening

   D. falling at a constant acceleration and terminal velocity

16. Two crates of medical supplies, labelled *A* and *B*, are dropped from a plane that is flying at a uniform velocity of 150 m/s. One second after crate *A* is dropped, crate *B* is dropped. Neglecting air resistance, crate *A* is

   A. vertically above crate *B*

   B. horizontally behind crate *B*

   C. horizontally ahead of crate *B*

   D. vertically under crate *B*

CHALLENGER QUESTION

17. A person walks 50 m to the east in 20 s, then 75 m to the west in 30 s, and finally 150 m to the east in 45 s. What is the person's average velocity?

   A. 0.35 m/s east

   B. 1.3 m/s east

   C. 0.76 m/s east

   D. 2.9 m/s east

18. Two rocks are thrown from a bridge. The first is thrown vertically upward, and the second is thrown vertically downward. Both rocks leave the throwers' hands at the same speed. On reaching the water below (ignoring air resistance), the first rock strikes the water with a velocity

   A. equal to that of the second rock

   B. less than that of the second rock

   C. greater than that of the second rock

   D. either greater or less depending on the masses of the rocks

Numerical Response

4. A zoologist fires a tranquilizer dart horizontally with a velocity of 15 m/s directly at a monkey sitting in a tree 20 m away. The dart passes below the monkey by a distance of _____ m. (Record your answer as a **two-digit** number.)

Use the following information to answer the next two questions.

A car drives 15 km north and 20 km west.

Numerical Response

5. The magnitude of its total displacement is _____ km. (Record your answer as a **two-digit** number.)

6. The direction of its total displacement is ___°W of N. (Record your answer as a **two-digit** number.)

Use the following information to answer the next two questions.

A bicyclist rides 200 m west, 120 m south, and 80.0 m east in 1.00 minute.

19. The average speed of the bicyclist is

   A. 2.83 m/s

   B. 6.67 m/s

   C. 10.7 m/s

   D. 14.3 m/s

20. The magnitude of the bicyclist's average velocity is

   A. 2.83 m/s

   B. 6.67 m/s

   C. 10.7 m/s

   D. 14.3 m/s

Use the following information to answer the next question.

A hiker walks 2.5 km at 25° N of E, then 3.4 km at 10° W of S.

Numerical Response

7. The magnitude of her total displacement is_____ km. ((Record your answer as a **two-digit** number.)

8. The direction of her total displacement is ____° E of S. (Record your answer as a **two-digit** number.)

21. A swimmer can swim at 4.00 km/h in still water. He heads south across a river that flows east at 2.00 km/h. The river is 0.500 km wide. His velocity with respect to the ground is

  A. 4.47 km/h 30.0° E of S

  B. 4.47 km/h 26.6° E of S

  C. 3.46 km/h 26.6° E of S

  D. 3.46 m/h 30.0° E of S

22. A pilot must fly 280 km from Calgary to Edmonton (assume that Edmonton is directly north of Calgary). His plane flies at 200 km/h and the wind blows steadily at 70.0 km/h from the west. How long will it take to complete the trip?

  A. 1.04 h   B. 1.32 h

  C. 1.40 h   D. 1.49 h

CHALLENGER QUESTION

23. On a cruise ship travelling 20° S of W at a speed of 6.0 m/s, a passenger jogs at 2.5 m/s east. What is the magnitude of the passenger's resultant velocity relative to Earth?

  A. 3.7 m/s   B. 5.7 m/s

  C. 6.5 m/s   D. 7.2 m/s

Written Response

Use the following information to answer the next question.

When something falls through the air, after a certain amount of time, it reaches what is called "terminal velocity." At this velocity, there is no longer any acceleration, and the object falls at a constant speed. This occurs because the force due to air resistance at this speed equals and opposes the gravitational force on the object. When skydivers jump out of an airplane, they initially accelerate toward Earth at 9.81 m/s^2. Suppose that the terminal velocity of skydiver Brian Heath is 55.6 m/s. When his parachute opens, it provides a deceleration of 30 m/s^2.

1. a) If the velocity at landing must be 5.0 m/s or less to avoid injury, what is the minimum height at which Brian, falling at terminal velocity, must open his parachute?

*Use this additional information to answer parts **b**) and **c**).*

> The feeling of downward acceleration (e.g., falling) can be described as an odd sensation in the pit of one's stomach. If Brian is skydiving and his altimeter is faulty (a very dangerous situation), he can still estimate part of the distance he has fallen through this feeling in his stomach.

b) If Brian stops feeling the sensation of acceleration 13.0 s after he leaves the airplane, how far has he fallen?
(Hint: Brian stops feeling the sensation of acceleration when he reaches terminal velocity.) (Assume uniform accelerated motion.)

*Use your answer from part **b**) to answer part **c**).*

c) It is usually dangerous to go below 300 m before opening the parachute. If Brian's jump (from part **b**)) is from an altitude of 1.20 km above the Earth's surface, how much time does he have to open his parachute safely (i.e., at 300 m)?

ANSWERS AND SOLUTIONS—PRACTICE QUESTIONS

1. D	9. A	16. D	NR8. 36
2. C	10. C	17. B	21. B
3. C	NR2. 1183	18. A	22. D
4. A	11. A	NR4. 8.7	23. A
NR1. 50	12. B	NR5. 25	WR1. See Solution
5. B	13. C	NR6. 53	
6. A	NR3. 7.25	19. B	
7. D	14. C	20. A	
8. D	15. D	NR7. 2.8	

1. D

A vector quantity has both magnitude and direction. Displacement has both magnitude and direction. On the other hand, mass, time and length are considered to be scalar quantities.

2. C

An $\bar{a}$-t graph indicating uniform acceleration would be a horizontal straight line, so graph **A** is wrong. A linear $\bar{v}$-t graph indicates uniform acceleration. Since the skydiver is decelerating, graph **B** is wrong (it shows velocity increasing, i.e., acceleration), and graph **C** is correct. A $\bar{d}$-t graph for uniform accelerated motion is curved, so graph **D** is wrong.

3. C

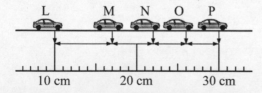

To determine which statement is incorrect, first determine which statements are possible descriptions of the car's motion.

Since you cannot determine with certainty from the picture whether the car was moving from left to right or right to left, statement **A** could be true.

By measuring the distances travelled between flashes, you should notice that $\overline{LM} > \overline{MN} > \overline{NO}$, which indicates that the car was moving faster at $\overline{LM}$ than at $\overline{NO}$. If the car was moving from left to right, then it was slowing from point L to point O. Therefore, statement **B** could be true.

If the car travelled at a constant velocity between points M and O, then the car's velocity between points M and N must be the same as its velocity between points N and O. It follows that if the velocity and time between points M and N and between points N and O are equal, $v_{MN} = v_{NO}$ and $t_{MN} = t_{NO}$, so d_{MN} should be equal to d_{NO}. (You can prove this using the equation $v = \dfrac{d}{t}$).

However, since $d_{MN} \neq d_{NO}$, then statement **C** is not a possible description of the motion of the car, (i.e., the car's speed was not constant between M and O).

Similarly, the car's velocity from point N to point O is the same as the velocity from point O to point P. Therefore, statement **D** could describe the motion of the car as shown in the image.

Therefore, statement **C** is not a possible description of the motion of the car.

4. A

Since the time between flashes is equal, a greater distance travelled by the car between flashes indicates a greater average speed. Pick a common reference point on the car to determine Δd.
From the diagram, LM = 7.0 cm, MN = 5.0 cm, NO = 4.0 cm, OP = 4.0 cm. Therefore, the greatest average speed was between L and M.

NR 1   50

Determining Δt can be tricky. There are 4 spaces of time (time intervals) between the 5 flashes.

$$\Delta t = \frac{4 \text{ flashes}}{10 \text{ flashes/s}}$$
$$= 0.40 \text{ s}$$

$$v_{average} = \frac{\Delta d}{\Delta t}$$
$$= \frac{30 \text{ cm} - 10 \text{ cm}}{0.40 \text{ s}}$$
$$= 50 \text{ cm/s}$$

This car also exhibits deceleration (travelling from left to right) as it covers less distance between flashes.

5. B

$$\vec{a} = \frac{\vec{v}_f - \vec{v}_i}{t}$$
$$= \frac{(0-150) \text{ km/h}}{2.00 \text{ s}}$$
$$= \frac{-150 \text{ km/h}}{2.00 \text{ s}} \times \frac{1.00 \text{ h}}{3\,600 \text{ s}} \times \frac{1\,000 \text{ m}}{1.00 \text{ km}}$$
$$= -20.8 \text{ m/s}^2$$

Note: Units can be very tricky. It is good practice to convert to standard units (kg, m, s).

Note: The acceleration is negative because the plane slows down.

6. A

Both graph **B** and graph **D** are incorrect because both show a maximum acceleration of 96.0 km/h^2.

However, an object accelerating from 0 to 96 km/h velocity in 3.89 s undergoes a much greater acceleration.

$$\vec{a}_{ave} = \frac{\Delta \vec{v}}{t}$$
$$= \frac{96.0 \text{ km/h}}{3.89 \text{ s}} \times \frac{3\,600 \text{ s}}{1.00 \text{ h}}$$
$$= 88\,843 \text{ km/h}^2$$
$$= 8.88 \times 10^4 \text{ km/h}^2$$

From the information given, $v = 0$ km/h when $t = 0$ s, and when $t = 3.89$ s, then $v = 96.0$ km/h. Therefore, graph **C** is also incorrect, since the line on the v-t graph does not go through the points (0, 0) and (3.89, 96.0). Graph **A** is the best choice since the line on the v-t graph passes through both points (0, 0) and (3.89, 96.0).

7. D

Any object in motion near Earth's surface while not on its surface is in free fall. The acceleration of an object in free fall is constant ($\vec{g} = -9.81$ m/s^2). Even when the object reaches maximum height, acceleration is still constant. Graph **D** shows the constant acceleration of the stone.

8. D

Since the trolley is powered by the force of gravity, i.e., a falling weight, the trolley will accelerate at a constant rate. If the trolley is accelerating, then velocity is increasing and the distance travelled should increase in each successive time interval. Since graph **A** shows the same distance travelled during each time interval, it is not correct. Graph **B** represents an object that slows down over time, so it is not correct. Graph **C** shows an object that is not moving, so it is not correct. Graph **D** is correct because it shows an object that is accelerating over time.

9. A

Since the object is accelerating at a constant rate (the acceleration is due to the falling weight), the velocity of the trolley will increase at a constant rate. Graph **A** shows a constant increase in velocity, and it is therefore the correct answer. Graph **B** is not correct because it shows velocity increasing, but at a greater rate at the beginning than at the end, whereas the velocity of the trolley increases at a constant rate. Graph **C** is not correct, because it shows a constant velocity. The trolley would experience acceleration, therefore, velocity must increase over time. Graph **D** is not correct because it shows a velocity increasing at an increasing rate, i.e. the object's acceleration is increasing with time.

10. C

The trolley is powered by a falling weight so acceleration would be a constant. Only graph **C** plots acceleration as a constant value (a straight horizontal line).

NR 2   1183

Note: As the object decelerates, $v = \dfrac{d}{t}$ cannot be used. In this solution, average speed is used.

$$d = \left(\frac{v_f + v_i}{2}\right)t$$

$$5.00 \times 10^3 \text{ m} = \left(\frac{0 \text{ m/s} + 8.50 \text{ m/s}}{2}\right)t$$

$$t = \left(5.00 \times 10^3 \text{ m}\right)\left(\frac{.2}{8.50 \text{ m/s}}\right)$$

$$t = 1.18 \times 10^3 \text{ s}$$

11. A

Graph **B** shows an object in uniform motion, therefore, its acceleration is zero; it is neither accelerating nor decelerating. Graph **C** shows a typical curve for a car's motion where acceleration is highest at the start. Graph **D** shows an object undergoing a rapid deceleration followed by a more constant velocity. Graph **A** is correct, because it shows a constant increase in velocity over time; that is, it shows constant acceleration.

12. B

$$v_f^2 = v_i^2 + 2ad$$

$$\left(515 \text{ km/h}\right)^2 = 0 + 2a\left(5.00 \text{ km}\right)$$

Magnitude of the average acceleration is

$$a = \frac{\left(515 \text{ km/h}\right)^2}{2\left(5.00 \text{ km}\right)} = 2.65 \times 10^4 \text{ km/h}^2$$

Note: It is easier to solve this problem in non-standard units. If it was necessary, the answer could have been converted at the end.

13. C

The area of the triangular area is $\dfrac{bh}{2}$.

The units being multiplied are seconds and metres per second. Therefore, the unit calculated for the shaded area is $s \times m/s = m$. Since m is a measure of distance or displacement, the shaded area under the velocity vs. time graph represents displacement.

NR 3   7253

$$v = \frac{\Delta d}{\Delta t}$$

$$\Delta d = \left(1\,450 \text{ m/s}\right)\left(\frac{10.0 \text{ s}}{2}\right)$$

$$= 7.25 \times 10^3 \text{ m}$$

Note: As the sea bed reflects the sonar impulse, the 10.0 s time interval is the time required for the signal to travel down to the sea bed and back to the boat. The time for the signal to travel one way is 5.0 s, as the motion is uniform.

14. C

First, find the time needed to go from the 10.0 m height to the water.

$$\bar{d} = \bar{v}_i t + \frac{1}{2}\bar{a}t^2$$

$$\bar{d} = \frac{1}{2}\bar{a}t^2 \ \left(\because \bar{v}_i = 0\right)$$

$$-10.0 \text{ m} = \frac{1}{2}\left(-9.81 \text{ m/s}^2\right)t^2$$

$$t^2 = \frac{2\left(-10.0 \text{ m}\right)}{-9.81 \text{ m/s}^2}$$

$$t = \sqrt{\frac{2\left(-10.0 \text{ m}\right)}{-9.81 \text{ m/s}^2}}$$

$$= 1.43 \text{ s}$$

Time for recording a complete dive
$= 1.43 \text{ s} + 1.00 \text{ s} + 1.00 \text{ s} = 3.43 \text{ s}$

$$\text{Number of dives } = \frac{30.0 \text{ min} \times 60.0 \text{ s/min}}{3.43 \text{ s}}$$

$$= 524.78 \text{ dives}$$

$$\doteq 524 \text{ dives}$$

Note: Since you are counting the number of dives, do not use significant digits. The answer should be rounded to the next lower whole number in order to calculate the number of completed dives.

15. D

Identify the various parts of the graph. Since phase I is the initial stage of the jump and shows the sky diver's velocity increasing at a constant rate, phase I would represent the initial period of free fall prior to reaching terminal velocity. Phase II represents a period of falling at a high constant velocity (approx. 200 km/h), which is referred to as terminal velocity. Phase III represents a period of very rapid deceleration, which would correspond to the parachute opening. Phase IV shows the sky diver continuing to fall, but at a considerably slower constant velocity, i.e., the parachute is open and the sky diver is floating to Earth. Therefore, phases I and II represent the skydiver falling at a constant acceleration and terminal velocity.

16. D

Neglecting air resistance, crate A will maintain the same forward velocity (150 m/s) as the plane, but it will fall vertically (due to gravity). Therefore, crate A will be directly under crate B.

17. B

$$\vec{d} = (+50 \text{ m}) + (-75 \text{ m}) + (+150 \text{ m})$$
$$= +125 \text{ m}$$
$$= 125 \text{ m east}$$
$$t = 20 \text{ s} + 30 \text{ s} + 45 \text{ s}$$
$$= 95 \text{ s}$$
$$\vec{v} = \frac{\vec{d}}{t}$$
$$= \frac{125 \text{ m}}{95 \text{ s}}$$
$$= 1.3 \text{ m/s east}$$

Note: Typically, west and south are labelled as negative to ease calculations. Here, the answer for velocity is positive indicating that the direction is east. If the question had asked for average speed and not velocity, no directions would be used, and the 75 m in the calculation of net distance would not be negative.

18. A

The velocity of the rock that was thrown upward will have a downward velocity equal to its initial upward velocity when it returns to the level at which it was thrown. As a result, both rocks will travel downward with the same velocity and with the same acceleration, and enter the water with the same velocity.

NR 4   8.7

Horizontal motion:

$$\vec{v} = \frac{\vec{d}}{t}$$
$$t = \frac{\vec{d}}{\vec{v}}$$
$$= \frac{20 \text{ m}}{15 \text{ m/s}}$$
$$= 1.33 \text{ s}$$

Vertical motion:

$$\vec{d} = \vec{v}_i t + \frac{1}{2}\vec{a}t^2$$
$$\vec{v}_i = 0 \quad \text{and} \quad \vec{a} = \vec{g}$$
$$\vec{d} = \frac{1}{2}\vec{g}t^2$$
$$= \frac{1}{2}(-9.81 \text{ m/s}^2)(1.33 \text{ s})^2$$
$$= -8.7 \text{ m, or 8.7 m below the monkey}$$

NR 5   25

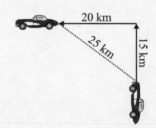

Use the Pythagorean theorem to calculate the magnitude of the total displacement.

$$d = \sqrt{(20 \text{ km})^2 + (15 \text{ km})^2}$$
$$= 25 \text{ km}$$

NR 6   53

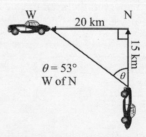

Use the tangent function to find the direction of the displacement.

$$\theta = \tan^{-1}\left(\frac{20 \text{ km}}{15 \text{ km}}\right)$$
$$= 53° \text{ W of N}$$

19. B

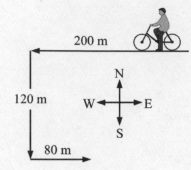

$$\text{average speed} = \frac{\text{total distance}}{\text{total time}}$$
$$= \frac{200 \text{ m} + 120 \text{ m} + 80.0 \text{ m}}{1.00 \text{ min}}$$
$$= \frac{400 \text{m}}{60.0 \text{s}}$$
$$= 6.67 \text{ m/s}$$

20. A

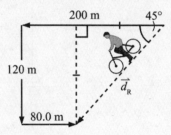

Determine the displacements along the horizontal and vertical directions.

$$\vec{d}_x = 200 \text{ m} - 80.0 \text{ m}$$
$$= +120 \text{ m}$$
$$\vec{d}_y = +120 \text{ m}$$

(considering west and south as positive)

Use the Pythagorean theorem to calculate the magnitude of the resultant displacement.

$$d_R = \sqrt{d_x^2 + d_y^2}$$
$$= \sqrt{(120 \text{ m})^2 + (120 \text{ m})^2}$$
$$= \sqrt{28\ 800 \text{ m}^2}$$
$$d_R = 169.7 \text{ m}$$

Determine the magnitude of the bicyclist' average velocity from the displacement and the time travelled.

$$v = \frac{d_R}{t}$$
$$= \frac{169.7 \text{ m}}{60.0 \text{ s}}$$
$$= 2.83 \text{ m/s}$$

NR 7   2.8

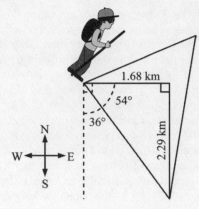

Find components of first displacement vector $\left(\vec{d}\right)$:

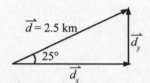

By convention, consider east and north directions to be positive.

$$d_y = d \sin 25°$$
$$= (2.5 \text{ km}) \sin 25°$$
$$= 1.057 \text{ km}$$
$$\therefore \vec{d}_y = 1.057 \text{ km north}$$

$$d_x = d \cos 25°$$
$$= (2.5 \text{ km}) \cos 25°$$
$$= 2.266 \text{ km}$$
$$\therefore \vec{d}_x = 2.266 \text{ km east}$$

Find components of the other vector $\left(\vec{d}'\right)$.

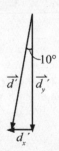

$$d_y' = d' \cos 10°$$
$$= (3.4 \text{ km}) \cos 10°$$
$$= 3.348 \text{ km}$$
$$\therefore \vec{d}_y' = 3.348 \text{ km south}$$

$$d_x' = d' \sin 10°$$
$$= (3.4 \text{ km}) \sin 10°$$
$$= 0.590 \text{ km}$$
$$\therefore \vec{d}_x' = 0.590 \text{ km west}$$

Add the horizontal components.

$$\vec{d}_{xR} = \vec{d}_x + \vec{d}_x'$$
$$= 2.266 \text{ km} - 0.590 \text{ km}$$
$$= +1.68 \text{ km east}$$

Add the vertical components.

$$\vec{d}_{yR} = \vec{d}_y + \vec{d}_y'$$
$$= 1.057 \text{ km} - 3.348 \text{ km}$$
$$= -2.29 \text{ km north or } 2.29 \text{ km south}$$

Put the totals together. They always make a right triangle.

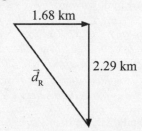

Use the Pythagorean theorem to determine the magnitude of the resultant displacement:

$$d_R = \sqrt{d_{xR}^2 + d_{yR}^2}$$
$$= \sqrt{(1.68 \text{ km})^2 + (2.29 \text{ km})^2}$$
$$= \sqrt{8.07 \text{ km}^2}$$
$$= 2.8 \text{ km}$$

NR 8   36

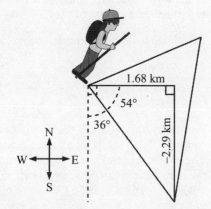

Use the tangent function to find the direction of hiker's total displacement.

$$\theta = \tan^{-1}\left(\frac{2.29 \text{ km}}{1.68 \text{ km}}\right)$$
$$= 54° \text{ S of E}$$
$$= 36° \text{ E of S}$$

21. B

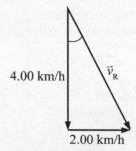

Consider south and east to be positive for this problem. Then use the Pythagorean theorem to determine the magnitude of velocity.

$$v_R = \sqrt{(4.00 \text{ km/h})^2 + (2.00 \text{ km/h})^2}$$
$$= 4.47 \text{ km/h}$$

Use the tangent function to find the direction of the resultant velocity.

$$\theta = \tan^{-1}\left(\frac{2.00 \text{ km/h}}{4.00 \text{ km/h}}\right)$$
$$= 26.6° \text{ E of S}$$

22. D

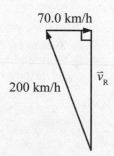

$$(200 \text{ km/h})^2 = (70.0 \text{ km/h})^2 + v_R^2$$
$$\text{so } v_R = \sqrt{(200 \text{ km/h})^2 - (70.0 \text{ km/h})^2}$$
$$= 187.35 \text{ km/h}$$
$$t = \frac{d}{v}$$
$$= \frac{280 \text{ km}}{187.35 \text{ km/h}}$$
$$= 1.49 \text{ h}$$

23. A

Find the components of the ship's velocity. Consider south and west to be positive for this problem.

$$v_x = (6.0 \text{ m/s}) \cos 20°$$
$$= 5.64 \text{ m/s}$$
$$\therefore \vec{v}_x = 5.64 \text{ m/s west}$$
$$v_y = (6.0 \text{ m/s}) \sin 20°$$
$$= 2.05 \text{ m/s}$$
$$\therefore \vec{v}_y = 2.05 \text{ m/s south}$$

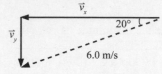

Find the net x and y components of velocities of the boat and of the passenger.

$$\vec{v}_{xR} = 5.64 \text{ m/s west} + 2.5 \text{ m/s east}$$
$$= 5.64 \text{ m/s west} - 2.5 \text{ m/s west}$$
$$= 3.14 \text{ m/s west}$$
$$\vec{v}_{yR} = 2.05 \text{ m/s south}$$
$$v_R = \sqrt{(3.14 \text{ m/s})^2 + (2.05 \text{ m/s})^2}$$
$$v_R = 3.7 \text{ m/s}$$

1.

a) *If the velocity at landing must be 5.0 m/s or less to avoid injury, what is the minimum height at which Brian, falling at terminal velocity, must open his parachute?*

$$v_f^2 = v_i^2 + 2ad$$
$$d = \frac{v_f^2 - v_i^2}{2a} \quad (a = -30 \text{ m/s}^2)$$
$$= \frac{(5.0 \text{ m/s})^2 - (55.6 \text{ m/s})^2}{2(-30 \text{ m/s}^2)}$$
$$= 51 \text{ m}$$

b) *If Brian stops feeling the sensation of acceleration 13.0 s after he leaves the airplane, how far has he fallen? (Hint: Brian stops feeling the sensation of acceleration when he reaches terminal velocity.) (Assume uniform accelerated motion.)*

$$\vec{d} = \left(\frac{\vec{v}_f + \vec{v}_i}{2}\right)t$$
$$= \left(\frac{55.6 \text{ m/s} + 0}{2}\right)(13.0 \text{ s})$$
$$= 361 \text{ m downward}$$

c) *It is usually dangerous to go below 300 m before opening the parachute. If Brian's jump is from an altitude of 1.20 km above the Earth's surface, how much time does he have to open his parachute safely (i.e., at 300 m)?*

The total distance Brian will travel from the airplane to the ground is 1 200 m. From part **b)**, you know that it will take Brian 361 m to reach terminal velocity.

You are also told that Brian will open the parachute at 300 m above the ground. Hence, for the remaining distance, Brian will be free falling at terminal velocity. Therefore, Brian can free fall for (1 200 m – 300 m – 361 m) = 539 m, at terminal velocity. The time it will take to fall 539 m at terminal velocity may be calculated using the formula $t = \dfrac{d}{v}$.

$$t = \frac{539 \text{ m}}{55.6 \text{ m/s}}$$
$$= 9.7 \text{ s}$$

From part **b)**, you know that it will take Brian 13.0 s to reach terminal velocity. Therefore, the total time before opening the parachute = (time to reach terminal velocity) + (time to fall 539 m at terminal velocity).

Total time = 13.0 s + 9.7 s = 22.7 s

UNIT TEST—KINEMATICS

1. An example of a scalar quantity is
   A. position
   B. gravity
   C. velocity
   D. temperature

Use the following information to answer the next question.

Scientists on the imaginary planet Q have defined a unit of length, the LAR, to be the distance between two mountain peaks on the surface of the planet. The unit of time on planet Q is called the TIK, and is defined as the average interval between the heart beats of the king.

2. Which of the following units would correctly express acceleration on planet Q?
   A. LAR/TIK
   B. TIK/LAR
   C. TIK/LAR^2
   D. LAR/TIK^2

Use the following information to answer the next question.

A "shooting star," or meteor, is a piece of interstellar rock that enters Earth's atmosphere at high velocity (approximately 40 km/s).

3. Given that Earth's atmosphere is 120 km thick, how long would a meteor, with a speed of 40 km/s, take to travel through the atmosphere to Earth's surface? (Assume no atmospheric friction or acceleration.)
   A. 0.33 s
   B. 3.0 s
   C. 4.8 s
   D. 10 s

Use the following graph to answer the next question.

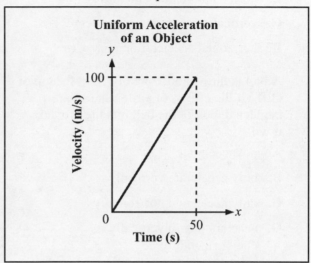

4. What is the acceleration of the object?
   A. 0.50 m/s^2
   B. 1.0 m/s^2
   C. 2.0 m/s^2
   D. 25 m/s^2

Use the following graph to answer the next question.

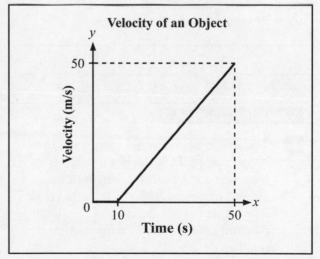

5. The acceleration of the object between 10 s and 50 s is
   A. 0.08 m/s^2
   B. 1.0 m/s^2
   C. 1.3 m/s^2
   D. 8.0 m/s^2

6. A bullet is fired horizontally. Neglecting the effects of air resistance, as the bullet travels outward, its

    A. vertical velocity increases

    B. horizontal velocity increases

    C. vertical acceleration increases

    D. horizontal acceleration increases

7. A ball is thrown horizontally from the top of a cliff. If the effects of air resistance are neglected, before the ball hits the ground, it will

    A. not accelerate

    B. only accelerate vertically

    C. only accelerate horizontally

    D. accelerate both vertically and horizontally

Use the following information to answer the next question.

The largest aircraft carrier in the world, the USS Nimitz, uses a catapult to launch its jets. Steam from the ship's reactor is used to accelerate jets to a high velocity over a short period of time.

CHALLENGER QUESTION

Numerical Response

1. The length of an aircraft carrier is 150 m. A jet taking off accelerates uniformly from rest and travels the length of the aircraft carrier in 2.00 s. The jet's velocity when it leaves the ship is _____ km/h. (Record your answer as a **three-digit** number.)

Use the following information to answer the next question.

An object that is thrown upward will eventually fall back to Earth unless the object reaches a very high velocity. This velocity is called the escape velocity, which is equal to 11.2 km/s.

8. A rocket takes off from the surface of Earth and accelerates uniformly until it reaches the "top" of the atmosphere, where its speed reaches 11.2 km/s. What is the average acceleration of the rocket, given that the distance it travels from the surface of Earth to the "top" of the atmosphere is 30 km?

    A. 0.19 km/s^2 B. 1.0 km/s^2

    C. 2.1 km/s^2 D. 4.2 km/s^2

Use the following information to answer the next question.

A new feature at the Olympic Games is the "dive camera" that tapes a diver's progress from the platform to under the water. The camera falls at the same free fall rate as the diver. (Assume initial velocity of the camera is zero.)

CHALLENGER QUESTION

Numerical Response

2. When the camera enters the water, it experiences a shock and a sudden deceleration by the water. If the camera was only designed to withstand a maximum shock corresponding to an entry speed of 16.0 m/s, then the maximum height from which the camera can fall is _____ m. (Record your answer as a **three-digit** number.)

A man walks from his house in a straight line at 2 m/s for 2 min and then sits down in a park for 10 min. He then returns along the same path to his house at 2 m/s.

9. Which of the following velocity-time graphs represents the man's motion?

A.

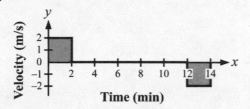

B.

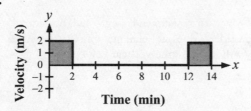

C.

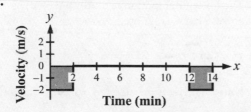

D.

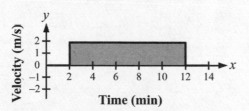

10. In a velocity versus time graph, when a person moves with uniform velocity, what does the shaded area on the graph between the line and the horizontal axis represent?

A. Distance

B. Velocity

C. Acceleration

D. Displacement

Use the following information to answer the next question.

The machine gun was invented in 1884 by Hiram Maxim. Modern machine guns, like the M2, fire 450 rounds per minute at a velocity of 860 m/s.

CHALLENGER QUESTION

11. How far will one of these bullets travel when fired from the ground at an angle of 10.5°? (Ignore air resistance.)

A. 4.78 km   B. 13.5 km

C. 27.0 km   D. 37.7 km

Use the following information to answer the next two questions.

A stone is thrown horizontally with a speed of 8.00 m/s from the top of a cliff that is 113 m high.

Numerical Response

3. The time, in seconds, that it takes the stone to reach the bottom of the cliff is _____ s. (Round and record your answer to **three digits**.)

12. How far from the base of the cliff does the stone land?

A. 1.75 m   B. 38.4 m

C. 113 m   D. 184 m

Use the following information to answer the next question.

A duck swimming at 0.80 m/s sets out straight across a 13 m wide river that is flowing east at 2.0 m/s.

Numerical Response

4. The duck will cross the river in _____ s. (Record your answer to **two digits**.)

ANSWERS AND SOLUTIONS—UNIT TEST

1. D	5. C	8. C	11. C
2. D	6. A	NR2. 13.0	NR3. 4.80
3. B	7. B	9. A	12. B
4. C	NR1. 540	10. D	NR4. 16

1. D

A scalar quantity has only magnitude (no direction). So temperature is a scalar quantity. **Note**: Change of position is also called displacement.

2. D

Acceleration is the rate of change of velocity, so any acceleration unit is a velocity unit divided by a time unit, or a distance unit divided by the product of two time units.

As $\vec{d}$ is in LAR and t is in TIK, then $\vec{a}$ would be measured in units of $\dfrac{\text{LAR}}{\text{TIK}^2}\left(\text{like } \dfrac{\text{m}}{\text{s}^2}\right)$.

3. B

$$v = \frac{d}{t}$$
$$t = \frac{d}{v}$$
$$= \frac{120 \text{ km}}{40 \text{ km/s}}$$
$$= 3.0 \text{ s}$$

4. C

Recall $\vec{a} = \dfrac{\Delta \vec{v}}{\Delta t} = \text{slope}$. The Δ indicates change, so the 0 s and 0 m/s should be shown in the calculation of $\vec{a}$.

$$\vec{a} = \text{slope}$$
$$= \frac{100 \text{ m/s} - 0 \text{ m/s}}{50 \text{ s} - 0 \text{ s}}$$
$$= +2.0 \text{ m/s}^2$$

5. C

$$\text{slope} = \vec{a}$$
$$= \frac{\Delta \vec{v}}{\Delta t}$$
$$= \frac{50 \text{ m/s} - 0 \text{ m/s}}{50 \text{ s} - 10 \text{ s}}$$
$$= +1.3 \text{ m/s}^2$$

6. A

Since air resistance is neglected, horizontal velocity does not change. Gravity, however, will increase the vertical velocity.

7. B

Gravity affects vertical motion only. The horizontal motion is uniform ($a = 0$) as air resistance is ignored.

NR 1   540

Note: The jet is accelerated, so $\vec{v} = \dfrac{\vec{d}}{t}$ cannot be used. In this solution, average velocity is used.

$$\vec{d} = \left(\frac{\vec{v}_{\text{f}} + \vec{v}_{\text{i}}}{2}\right) t \quad [\vec{v}_{\text{i}} = 0]$$
$$\Rightarrow \vec{v}_{\text{f}} = \frac{2\vec{d}}{t}$$
$$= \frac{2(150 \text{ m})}{2.00 \text{ s}}$$
$$= 150 \text{ m/s}$$
$$\therefore \vec{v}_{\text{f}} = \frac{150 \text{ m}}{1 \text{ s}} \times \frac{1 \text{ km}}{1\,000 \text{ m}} \times \frac{3\,600 \text{ s}}{1 \text{ h}}$$
$$= 540 \text{ km/h forward}$$

8. C

$$v_f^2 = v_i^2 + 2ad$$
$$(11.2 \text{ km/s})^2 = 0 + 2a(30 \text{ km})$$
$$a = \frac{(11.2 \text{ km/s})^2 - 0}{2(30 \text{ km})}$$
$$= 2.1 \text{ km/s}^2$$

Magnitude of acceleration is 2.1 km/s^2.

NR 2   13.0

There are two methods for solving this problem.

Method 1

$$v_f^2 = v_i^2 + 2ad \qquad (v_i^2 = 0)$$
$$d = \frac{v_f^2}{2g} \qquad (a = g)$$
$$= \frac{(16.0 \text{ m/s})^2}{2(9.81 \text{ m/s}^2)}$$
$$= 13.0 \text{ m}$$

Method 2

Find the time required to reach 16 m/s.

$$v_f = v_i + at$$
$$16.0 \text{ m/s} = 0 + (9.81 \text{ m/s}^2)t$$
$$t = \frac{16.0 \text{ m/s}}{9.81 \text{ m/s}^2}$$
$$t = 1.63 \text{ s}$$

Find the distance travelled in this time.

$$d = v_i t + \frac{1}{2}at^2$$
$$= 0 + \frac{1}{2}(9.81 \text{ m/s}^2)(1.63 \text{ s})^2$$
$$= 13.0 \text{ m}$$

9. A

As velocity has direction, the return trip is considered a negative because it is in the opposite direction of the initial velocity. Graph **B** is wrong. It is, at best, a speed-time graph since it correctly records the man's speed but does not account for the change of direction. Graph **C** is wrong because all values are negative, indicating no change in direction. Graph **D** is wrong because it indicates continuous motion when the man is resting. Graph **A** shows a constant velocity of 2 m/s for 2 two-minute intervals, which accurately represents the man's movements.

10. D

All the areas are rectangular in shape for uniform velocity in a velocity–time graph. Recall that area of a rectangle = $l \times w$. It follows that the area under the curve of a velocity–time graph (one that is rectangular in shape) = $t \times v$, as time is the length and velocity is the width of the area under the curve.

Since $d = v \times t$, the answer can only be distance or displacement. Since displacement is a vector quantity like velocity, and distance is scalar, then the shaded area on the graph represents displacement.

11. C

A projectile problem is solved like two independent linear problems. Determine the horizontal and vertical components of the bullet's velocity.

$$v_{ix} = (860 \text{ m/s})\cos(10.5)$$
$$= 845.6 \text{ m/s}$$
$$\therefore \vec{v}_{ix} = +845.6 \text{ m/s}$$
$$v_{iy} = (860 \text{ m/s})\sin(10.5)$$
$$= 156.7 \text{ m/s}$$
$$\therefore \vec{v}_{iy} = +156.7 \text{ m/s}$$

Gravity acts only on the vertical components.

$$\vec{d}_y = \vec{v}_{iy}t + \frac{1}{2}\vec{a}t^2$$
$$0 = (156.7 \text{ m/s})t + \frac{1}{2}(-9.81 \text{ m/s}^2)t^2$$
$$-\frac{1}{2}(-9.81 \text{ m/s}^2)t^2 = (156.7 \text{ m/s})t$$
$$\frac{1}{2}(9.81 \text{ m/s}^2)t = (156.7 \text{ m/s})$$
$$t = \frac{2(156.7 \text{ m/s})}{9.81 \text{ m/s}^2}$$
$$= 31.95 \text{ s}$$

There is no acceleration horizontally, assuming no air resistance.

Thus, $\vec{d} = \vec{v}t$ can be used.

$$\vec{d}_x = \vec{v}_{ix}t$$
$$= (845.6 \text{ m/s})(31.95 \text{ s})$$
$$= 27\,017 \text{ m}$$
$$= 27.0 \text{ km}$$

NR 3   4.80

Distance travelled in the vertical direction:

$$d = v_i t + \frac{1}{2} a t^2$$

$v_i = 0$ so

$$t = \sqrt{\frac{2d}{a}}$$

$$t = \sqrt{\frac{2 \times (113 \text{ m})}{(9.81 \text{ m/s}^2)}}$$

$$t = 4.80 \text{ s}$$

12. B

Distance travelled in vertical motion:

$$d = v_i t + \frac{1}{2} a t^2$$

$v_i = 0$ so

$$t = \sqrt{\frac{2d}{a}}$$

$$t = \sqrt{\frac{2 \times (113 \text{ m})}{(9.81 \text{ m/s}^2)}}$$

$$t = 4.80 \text{ s}$$

Use the constant horizontal speed to determine the range.

$$d = vt$$
$$= 8.00 \text{ m/s} \times 4.80 \text{ s}$$
$$= 38.4 \text{ m}$$

The stone lands at a distance 38.4 m from the bottom of the cliff.

NR 4   16

Since the duck heads directly across the river, it will cross at a speed 0.80 m/s no matter how far downstream it is carried.

$$t = \frac{d}{v}$$
$$= \frac{13 \text{ m}}{0.80 \text{ m/s}}$$
$$= 16 \text{ s}$$

DYNAMICS

Table of Correlations				
Specific Expectation	**Practice Questions**	**Unit Test Questions**	**Practice Test 1**	**Practice Test 2**
Students will:				
B1 Explain the effects of balanced and unbalanced forces on velocity.				
B1.1 explain that a non-zero net force causes a change in velocity	3, 15, 16	NR3, 11	12, 13	8
B1.2 apply Newton's first law of motion to explain, qualitatively, an object's state of rest or uniform motion	1, 2, 5	1, 3		9, 15
B1.3 apply Newton's second law of motion to explain, qualitatively, the relationships among net force, mass, and acceleration	NR1, 7	4, 9, 10	NR4	11
B1.4 apply Newton's third law of motion to explain, qualitatively, the interaction between two objects, recognizing that the two forces, equal in magnitude and opposite in direction, do not act on the same object	4, 6	5		NR5
B1.5 explain, qualitatively and quantitatively, static and kinetic forces of friction acting on an object	NR4, NR5, 11, 12	2, NR4	15, NR3	NR13
B1.6 calculate the resultant force, or its constituents, acting on an object by adding vector components graphically and algebraically	NR2, 8, NR3	6, 7, NR1	16, 17	12, NR7
B1.7 apply Newton's laws of motion to solve, algebraically, linear motion problems in horizontal, vertical and inclined planes near the surface of Earth, ignoring air resistance	9, 10, 13, NR6, 14, WR1, WR2	8, NR2	14, 18, NR5, NR6	10, NR6, 13, 14, WR1
B2 Explain that gravitational effects extend throughout the universe.				
B2.1 identify the gravitational force as one of the fundamental forces in nature	17, 21	NR5	27	NR8
B2.2 describe, qualitatively and quantitatively, Newton's law of universal gravitation	17, 21	NR5	27	NR8
B2.3 explain, qualitatively, the principles pertinent to the Cavendish experiment used to determine the universal gravitational constant, G	18	13		
B2.4 define the term "field" as a concept that replaces "action at a distance," and apply the concept to describe gravitational effects	NR9	15		
B2.5 relate, qualitatively and quantitatively, using Newton's law of universal gravitation, the gravitational constant to the local value of the acceleration due to gravity	NR7, 19	12		19, 22
B2.6 predict, quantitatively, differences in the weight of objects on different planets	20, NR8	14		20

DYNAMICS

B1.1 explain that a non-zero net force causes a change in velocity

FORCES AND THEIR EFFECTS

A force is any push or a pull on an object. It has both magnitude and direction, which means that it is a vector. It affects motion only in a cumulative way. That is, resulting motion comes from a net force. A net force is the vector sum of all forces acting on an object. If two forces on an object are equal and opposite to one another, it is as if no force acts at all on the object. If the net force is not equal to zero, then the object being pushed or pulled will change the way it is moving (i.e., acceleration).

There are several kinds of forces. Some examples of forces are:

* friction

* tension (a force exerted through a string, cable, etc.)

* normal force (a force exerted by a surface as a result of an object pushing on that surface)

* other types of forces are often referred to as applied forces (it is like having a miscellaneous category)

* gravitational force

The force of gravity on an object is usually referred to as the object's weight. This force is equal to the mass of the object multiplied by the acceleration due to gravity.

$$\vec{F}_g = m\vec{g}$$

Example

What is the mass of an object that weighs –150 N on Earth?

In this case the downward direction is chosen to be negative.

$$\vec{F}_g = m\vec{g}$$
$$-150\text{ N} = m\left(-9.81\text{ m/s}^2\right)$$
$$m = 15.3\text{ kg}$$

Example

What is the weight of a crate with a mass of 250 kg resting on the floor?

$$\vec{F}_g = m\vec{g}$$
$$= \left(250\text{ kg}\right)\left(-9.81\text{ m/s}^2\right)$$
$$= -2\ 453\text{ N}$$
$$= -2.45\text{ kN}$$

If the downward direction were chosen to be positive then the weight of the crate would simply be 2.45 kN.

Identifying all the forces acting on an object is one of the most important tasks when studying motion.

Example

Identify the forces acting on the objects in each of the following diagrams.

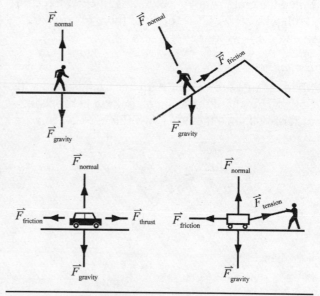

Practice Questions: 3, 15, 16

B1.2 apply Newton's first law of motion to explain, qualitatively, an object's state of rest or uniform motion

NEWTON'S FIRST LAW OF MOTION

Newton's first law states that a body continues in its state of rest or motion unless acted upon by a non-zero net force. Newton's first law is difficult to observe here on Earth. In space, an object that is set in motion will continue to move in a straight line indefinitely, unless another force acts to change the way it is moving. Any object at rest will remain at rest unless some force acts to change that.

Example

A 150 N force is used to drag a heavy crate across the floor at a constant speed. How much friction force is acting on this crate?

Since the crate is not accelerating, the net force on it must be zero. Therefore, the force of friction must be 150 N to the left.

Example

Sheila is in a tug-of-war with her friends Fred and Sally. How hard must Sheila pull on her rope in order to balance the other two forces?

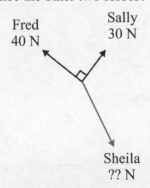

If nobody is moving, the sum of the forces must be zero. The Pythagorean theorem can be used to find the resultant of Fred and Sally's force.

$$F_R^2 = F_1^2 + F_2^2$$
$$= (30\text{ N})^2 + (40\text{ N})^2$$
$$= 900\text{ N}^2 + 1\,600\text{ N}^2$$
$$F_R^2 = 2\,500\text{ N}^2$$
$$F_R = 50\text{ N}$$

Sheila must pull with a force of 50 N in a direction opposite to the resultant of Fred's and Sally's force.

Practice Questions: 1, 2, 5

B1.3 apply Newton's second law of motion to explain, qualitatively, the relationships among net force, mass and acceleration

NEWTON'S SECOND LAW OF MOTION

Newton's second law states that a non-zero net force will accelerate an object. The acceleration of the object is directly proportional to the net force acting on it and is inversely proportional to its mass. The direction of the acceleration is in the direction of the net force acting on the object. This can be shown mathematically:

$$\vec{a} = \frac{\vec{F}}{m} \text{ or } \vec{F} = m\vec{a}$$

Newton's second law can be illustrated by an example of a person pushing a car that has run out of gas. It will take some effort, but the car (mass) can be made to roll (accelerate) in the direction that it is pushed (net force).

Example

A baseball is thrown at an empty pop can. Then it is thrown at the same speed at a full pop can. Explain why the empty pop can goes flying faster than the full one does.

The acceleration of each can is inversely proportional to the mass given that the force is the same for both. The empty can is a smaller mass than the full can. Therefore, it will have a larger acceleration than the full can.

Practice Questions: NR1, 7

B1.4 apply Newton's third law of motion to explain, qualitatively, the interaction between two objects, recognizing that the two forces, equal in magnitude and opposite in direction, do not act on the same object

NEWTON'S THIRD LAW OF MOTION

Newton's third law states that for every action, there is an equal and opposite reaction. Whenever one object exerts a force on a second object, the second object exerts an equal and opposite force on the first. Newton's third law can be illustrated by a ball that hits and bounces off a wall. The ball exerts a force on the wall, but the wall exerts a force back on the ball at the same time. The magnitude of the action and reaction forces are equal, but in the opposite direction. Note that the forces act on different objects.

Example

In each situation, identify the two equal and opposite forces:

a) A person jumps off the back of a boat. The boat drifts in the opposite direction of the person.

The person pushes on the boat, and the boat pushes back on the person.

b) A person does a standing long jump from a gym floor.

The person pushes back on the floor with friction, while the floor pushes the person forward, also with friction.

c) A penny falls from a table.

The gravity of Earth pulls the penny down while the gravity of the penny pulls Earth upward.

Practice Questions: 4, 6

B1.5   *explain, qualitatively and quantitatively, static and kinetic forces of friction acting on an object*

KINETIC AND STATIC FRICTION

Friction is a force that acts between two surfaces in a way that prevents them from sliding past one another. Friction is caused by intermolecular forces between the atoms and molecules of the two surfaces. Friction can exist between surfaces that are solid, liquid, or gas.

The amount of friction that exists between two solid surfaces is determined by how hard the

surfaces are pressed together and by how "sticky" the two surfaces actually are. When surfaces are pressed together, they exert normal forces on one another. The magnitude of the friction force is directly proportional to the magnitude of the normal force exerted by the surfaces.

The constant of proportionality between these forces is called the coefficient of friction. It is a measure of how "sticky" the two surfaces are. This can be stated algebraically as $|\vec{F}_f| = \mu |\vec{F}_N|$.

For simplicity, this is often stated as $F_f = \mu F_N$.

The Greek letter mu (μ) is the coefficient of friction. It has no unit.

The graph of the friction force as a function of the normal force is a straight line through the origin with a slope equal to μ.

When a surface, such as a book on a table, is pulled by a string attached to a spring scale, the spring scale will measure the force of friction. Typically, as the force on the scale increases, the book will remain at rest until it slips at some maximum force. Once it is moving, less force is needed to keep the book moving at a constant speed. In both cases, the net force on the book is zero, so the force on the scale is equal in magnitude to the friction force. There are two kinds of friction.

- **Static friction** (μ_s)—between surfaces that are not sliding past one another.

- **Kinetic** (or sliding) **friction** (μ_k)—between two surfaces that are sliding past one another.

Example

The coefficient of sliding friction between floor and a person's shoes is 0.32. Find the force of friction if the person's mass is 45 kg.

The magnitude of the force of friction is
$$F_f = \mu_k F_N$$
$$= (0.32)(45 \text{ kg})(9.81 \text{ m/s}^2)$$
$$= 141 \text{ kg} \cdot \text{m/s}^2$$
$$= 141 \text{ N}$$
$$= 1.4 \times 10^2 \text{ N}$$

Practice Questions: NR4, NR5, 11, 12

B1.6 *calculate the resultant force, or its constituents, acting on an object by adding vector components graphically and algebraically*

CALCULATION OF THE NET FORCE

Tom pushes and Fred pulls a fridge to the right against friction, as shown. Tom's force is 150 N, Fred's is 120 N, and the force of friction is 50 N. Find the net force on the fridge.

$$\vec{F}_{net} = 150\text{ N} + 120\text{ N} - 50\text{ N}$$
$$= 220\text{ N to the right}$$

Example

A boat is pulled by two ropes, one from each side of the river. Determine the net force acting on the boat in the following diagram.

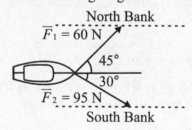

North Bank

$\vec{F}_1 = 60$ N

45°

30°

$\vec{F}_2 = 95$ N

South Bank

Consider east and north to be positive.

$\vec{F}_1$	$\vec{F}_2$
Horizontal: $F_{1x} = F_1 \cos 45°$ $= (60\text{ N})\cos 45°$ $= 42.4\text{ N}$	$F_{2x} = F_2 \cos(-30°)$ $= (95\text{ N})\cos(-30°)$ $= 82.3\text{ N}$
Vertical: $F_{1y} = F_1 \sin 45°$ $= (60\text{ N})\sin 45°$ $= 42.4\text{ N}$	$F_{2y} = F_2 \sin(-30°)$ $= (95\text{ N})\sin(-30°)$ $= -47.5\text{ N}$

Vector addition of components:

Horizontal
42.4 N + 82.3 N = 124.7 N east

Vertical
42.4 N – 47.5 N = –5.1 N
= 5.1 N south

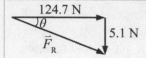

Not to scale

Magnitude of resultant force:

$$F_R = \sqrt{(124.7\text{ N})^2 + (5.1\text{ N})^2}$$
$$= 124.8\text{ N}$$
$$= 1.2 \times 10^2\text{ N}$$

Direction:

$$\theta = \tan^{-1}\left(\frac{5.1\text{ N}}{124.8\text{ N}}\right)$$
$$= 2.3°\text{ south of east.}$$

The net force is 1.2×10^2 N 2.3° S of E.

Practice Questions: NR2, 8, NR3

B1.7 *apply Newton's laws of motion to solve, algebraically, linear motion problem in horizontal, vertical and inclined planes near the surface of Earth, ignoring air resistance*

APPLICATIONS OF NEWTON'S LAWS

Newton's laws discuss the fundamentals of dynamics. These laws can be applied in day-to-day life, in different physical situations.

Example

A person pushes a 50.0-kg model car with a force of 250 N. The car accelerates at 2.00 m/s². Find the force of friction on the car.

First, draw a free-body diagram of the situation. This is a diagram showing the forces acting on the object in question. It is also a good idea to indicate the direction of the acceleration that results.

$$\vec{F}_{net} = \sum \vec{F}_{acting\ on\ object} \qquad \vec{F}_{net} = m\vec{a}$$

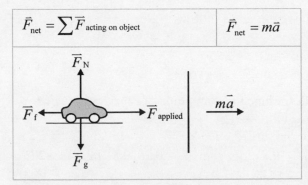

It is customary to show the forces as moving away from the object's center of gravity.

The normal force is equal to the weight.

The vector on the right labelled "$m\vec{a}$" is equal to the net force.

In this case, the applied force is greater than the friction force because the acceleration is in the direction of the applied force. It follows that:

$$\vec{F}_{applied} + \vec{F}_{f} = \vec{F}_{net}$$
$$\vec{F}_{f} = \vec{F}_{net} - \vec{F}_{applied}$$
$$\vec{F}_{f} = m\vec{a} - \vec{F}_{applied}$$
$$= (50.0\ kg)(2.00\ m/s^2) - 250\ N$$
$$= -150\ N$$

So frictional force is directed opposite to the applied force.

Example

A 60.0 kg person is standing in an elevator. As the elevator starts upward she seems to feel heavier for a moment. If she seems to weigh 620 N, find the acceleration of the elevator.

First, draw the free-body diagram.

$\vec{F}$	$= m\vec{a}$
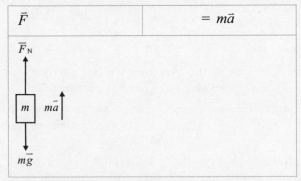	

Notice that the normal force from the floor has to push harder upward than the force of gravity pulls downward on the person. This causes the net upward acceleration.

The sensation of weight has to do with gravity; however, you don't sense gravity. Instead, you sense any forces that prevent gravity from accelerating your body. (If someone jumps off a roof, they would feel weightless all the way down to the ground.)

Most physics texts use the term "apparent weight" to describe the sensation of heaviness that you feel. The apparent weight in this case is equal to the normal force. It follows that:

$$\vec{F}_{N} + \vec{F}_{g} = \vec{F}_{net}$$
$$\vec{F}_{N} + m\vec{g} = m\vec{a}$$
$$\vec{a} = \frac{\vec{F}_{N} + m\vec{g}}{m}$$
$$= \frac{620\ N + (60.0\ kg)(-9.81\ m/s^2)}{60.0\ kg}$$
$$= \frac{620\ kg \cdot m/s^2 - 588.6\ kg \cdot m/s^2}{60.0\ kg}$$
$$= 0.523\ m/s^2\ upward$$

Example

Create a free-body diagram for a crate on a ramp inclined at 25°, where the crate has a mass of 35 kg and an unknown coefficient of friction μ_s. The crate is not accelerating. Find the coefficient of sliding friction.

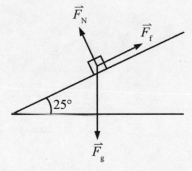

The gravitational force has components perpendicular to and parallel to the ramp. The perpendicular component of gravity is what pushes the surfaces together. It is therefore equal to the normal force.

Calculate the magnitude of the normal force.

$$F_{N} = F_{g} \cos 25°$$
$$F_{N} = mg \cos 25°$$
$$= (35\ kg)(9.81\ m/s^2) \cos 25°$$
$$= 311\ N$$

The component of gravity parallel to the ramp is the force trying to slide the object down the ramp. If the force of friction is equal to this force, then the object will not accelerate down the ramp.

Calculate the magnitude of the frictional force.

$F_f = F_g \sin 25°$

$F_f = mg \sin 25°$

$\quad = (35 \text{ kg})(9.81 \text{ m/s}^2)\sin 25°$

$\quad = 145 \text{ N}$

Now, use the formula for friction to find the coefficient of static friction.

$F_f = \mu_s F_N$

$\Rightarrow \mu_s = \dfrac{F_f}{F_N}$

$\quad = \dfrac{145 \text{ N}}{311 \text{ N}}$

$\quad = 0.47$

Example

A 75 kg skier skis down a 27° angle slope. If the coefficient of friction is 0.10, what is the skier's acceleration down the hill?

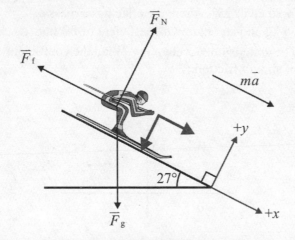

The component of gravity parallel to the slope is greater than the force of friction, so the acceleration is parallel to the slope. From a vector point of view looking at components parallel to the slope:

$\vec{F}_{g\,parallel} + \vec{F}_f = \vec{F}_{net}$

Since the frictional force is directed opposite to the parallel component of the gravitational force, considering only the magnitude, the equation can

be rewritten as follows:

$$F_{g\,parallel} - F_f = ma$$
$$mg \sin 27° - \mu mg \cos 27° = ma$$
$$g \sin 27° - \mu g \cos 27° = a$$

Determine the magnitude of acceleration down the hill.

$a = g \sin 27° - \mu g \cos 27°$

$a = (9.81 \text{ m/s}^2)\sin 27° - 0.10(9.81 \text{ m/s}^2)\cos 27°$

$\quad = 3.6 \text{ m/s}^2$

Practice Questions: 9, 10, 13, NR6, 14, WR1, WR2

B2.1 *identify the gravitational force as one of the fundamental forces in nature*

B2.2 *describe, qualitatively and quantitatively, Newton's law of universal gravitation*

NEWTON'S LAW OF UNIVERSAL GRAVITATION

There are four fundamental forces operating in the universe. Two of them (the strong and weak forces) are involved in holding atoms together. The electromagnetic force acts between charged particles and the fourth fundamental force is gravity. Gravity is a force that acts between any two masses and is always attractive.

Isaac Newton had difficulty explaining how two objects can exert a force between each other without touching each other. He referred to this as "action at a distance." He proposed that this force is directly proportional to the product of the two masses, and inversely proportional to the square of the distance between them. This can be expressed

algebraically as: $|\vec{F}_g| = G\dfrac{m_1 m_2}{r^2}$

In this formula, the G is the universal gravitational constant. The value of G has been found to be $6.67 \times 10^{-11} \text{ N} \cdot \text{m}^2/\text{kg}^2$.

Example

Find the force of gravity between a 40 kg person and 50 kg person when they are 2.0 m apart.

$$F_g = G\frac{m_1 m_2}{r^2}$$

$$= \frac{\left(6.67 \times 10^{-11}\,\frac{\text{N} \cdot \text{m}^2}{\text{kg}^2}\right)(40\text{ kg})(50\text{ kg})}{(2.0\text{ m})^2}$$

$$= 3.3 \times 10^{-8}\text{ N}$$

This is an extremely small force. The reason you do not notice it is because the force of gravity between Earth and your body is so much greater.

Example

Find the force of gravity between a 40 kg person and Earth.

$$F_g = G\frac{m_E m_p}{r_E^2}$$

$$= \frac{\left(6.67 \times 10^{-11}\,\frac{\text{N} \cdot \text{m}^2}{\text{kg}^2}\right)(5.98 \times 10^{24}\text{ kg})(40\text{ kg})}{(6.37 \times 10^6\text{ m})^2}$$

$$= 3.9 \times 10^2\text{ N}$$

In circular motion, acceleration is directed toward the center of the circular motion. This must also be true for celestial bodies, such as Earth and the moon. Since no physical tie exists between the two, gravity must be the force keeping them moving relative to one another.

Practice Questions: 17, 21

B2.3　*explain, qualitatively, the principles pertinent to the Cavendish experiment used to determine the universal gravitational constant, G*

DETERMINATION OF THE GRAVITATIONAL CONSTANT

The Cavendish experiment was designed to measure the universal gravitational constant. Two masses are attached to a thin rod suspended from a wire. When a third mass is brought close to the masses, the gravitational force between them causes the apparatus to move in a twisting motion. This is called a torsion balance. The wire's twist is converted to the force to be measured. The distance between the third mass and the suspended masses is measured and used

in the following equation:

$$G = \frac{F_g r^2}{m_1 m_2}$$

Practice Question: 18

B2.4　*define the term "field" as a concept that replaces "action at a distance" and apply the concept to describe gravitational effects*

B2.5　*relate, qualitatively and quantitatively, using Newton's Law of Universal Gravitation, the gravitational constant to the local value of the acceleration due to gravity*

GRAVITATION AS A FORCE FIELD

One way to explain Newton's "action at a distance" is to adopt the mathematical model called a field. The gravitational field is a "sphere of influence" around a mass in which another mass will feel a gravitational force. Gravitational fields are vector fields, meaning that they have both magnitude and direction. The direction is toward the centre of the mass that produced the field. The magnitude of a gravitational field is given with the formula:

$g = \dfrac{Gm}{r^2}$, where r = the distance from the centre

of the mass to the position in space where the field is measured, and m = the mass that produced the field.

Notice that the field gets weaker and weaker as you move farther from the mass that produced it. This is also an inverse square relationship.

This formula is most often used when trying to find the gravitational field at the surface of a planet, moon, or star.

Example

Find the gravitational field of Earth.

$$g = \frac{Gm_E}{r_E^2}$$

$$g = \frac{Gm_E}{r_E^2}$$

$$= \frac{\left(6.67 \times 10^{-11} \frac{N \cdot m^2}{kg^2}\right)\left(5.98 \times 10^{24}\ kg\right)}{\left(6.37 \times 10^6\ m\right)^2}$$

$$= 9.83\ N/kg$$

The unit N/kg is equivalent to the unit m/s^2.

The value of $9.81\ m/s^2$ is the standard average of the force of gravity across Earth's surface.

The force of gravity is actually greatest at Earth's poles for two reasons. The first is that Earth is not a perfect sphere, and therefore not all points on its surface are the same distance from the centre of the mass generating Earth's gravitational field. The second is that, because of the planet's rotation in space, objects on the surface of Earth are being acted upon by a force that acts at a perpendicular angle to the pull of the gravitational field.

The net effect is that the acceleration of an object due to gravity on the surface of Earth ranges from about $9.780\ m/s$ at the equator to roughly $9.832\ m/s$ at the poles, or a variation of 0.5%.

Practice Questions: NR7, NR9, 19

B2.6   predict, quantitatively, differences in the weight of objects on different planets

FORCE DUE TO GRAVITY ON DIFFERENT PLANETS

The weight of an object is found by multiplying its mass by the strength of the gravitational field that it is in. On Earth's surface, use $9.81\ m/s^2$. For other planets, calculate the gravitational field strength there.

Example

A man who has a mass of 75.0 kg on Earth has a different weight on the moon. Find his approximate weight on both surfaces.

Note: $m_{moon} = 7.35 \times 10^{22}\ kg$

$\qquad r_{moon} = 1.74 \times 10^6\ m$

Calculate the weight of the man on Earth, considering downward as the positive direction.

$$\vec{F}_{g(Earth)} = m\vec{g}$$
$$= \left(75.0\ kg\right)\left(9.81\ m/s^2\right)$$
$$= 7.36 \times 10^2\ N$$

$$g_{moon} = \frac{Gm_{moon}}{r_{moon}^2}$$

$$g = \frac{\left(6.67 \times 10^{11} \frac{N \cdot m^2}{kg^2}\left(7.35 \times 10^{22}\ kg\right)\right)}{\left(1.74 \times 10^6\ m\right)^2}$$

$$= 1.619\ m/s^2$$

The direction of the acceleration due to gravity is the same as the direction of the force of gravity. Find the weight of the man on the moon.

$$\vec{F}_{g(moon)} = m\vec{g}_{moon}$$
$$= \left(75.0\ kg\right)\left(1.619\ m/s^2\right)$$
$$= 1.21 \times 10^2\ N$$

Practice Questions: 20, NR8

PRACTICE QUESTIONS—DYNAMICS

Use the following information to answer the next question.

The diagram below represents a body moving along a horizontal surface with only two forces, shown as $\vec{F}_1$ and $\vec{F}_2$, affecting its motion.

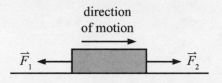

direction
of motion

$\vec{F}_1$ ←   → $\vec{F}_2$

CHALLENGER QUESTION

1. If the body is slowing down, then
   A. $\vec{F}_1 > \vec{F}_2$
   B. $\vec{F}_1 < \vec{F}_2$
   C. $\vec{F}_1 = \vec{F}_2$
   D. $\vec{F}_2 - \vec{F}_1 = 0$

Use the following information to answer the next question.

A motorist who runs out of gas starts to push his car to a nearby gas station. He finds that it is more difficult to get the car moving than it is to keep it moving.

2. This fact is described by
   A. Kepler's first law
   B. Kepler's third law
   C. Newton's first law
   D. Newton's third law

Numerical Response

1. A parked logging truck with a total mass of 5 200 kg starts moving with an acceleration of 2.0 m/s². The net force required to start the truck moving is _____ kN.
(Record your answer to **two** significant digits.)

Use the following information to answer the next question.

Iceboats are sailboats that rest evenly on three skates, enabling them to sail on ice. The total weight of the boat over the small surface area of the three skates causes some ice to melt. The skates, therefore, run on a thin layer of water, thereby reducing resistance.

3. If an iceboat has a mass of 150 kg, what is the force each skate places on the ice? (Assume that the weight of the iceboat is evenly distributed over the three skates.)
   A. 150 N
   B. 491 N
   C. 1.47 kN
   D. 4.41 kN

Use the following information to answer the next two questions.

Hang gliders are able to fly because of two principles. The first is Bernoulli's principle, which states that air flowing over the top of the wing moves faster than air below the wing. This difference in speeds creates lift in the wing.

The second principle states that air being forced down by the wing creates an equal but opposite force lifting up on the wing.

4. What is the name of this second principle?
   A. Kepler's first law
   B. Kepler's third law
   C. Newton's first law
   D. Newton's third law

Use the following information to answer the next three questions.

Sir Isaac Newton was responsible for a number of scientific laws that have been named after him. Some of these are:

I Newton's first law of motion

II Newton's second law of motion

III Newton's third law of motion

IV Newton's law of universal gravitation

5. When a car has a head-on collision, a passenger who is not wearing a seat belt may go through the windshield. Which of Newton's laws explains this?
   A. First
   B. Second
   C. Third
   D. Gravitation

6. Which of Newton's laws explains why a rifle recoils, or kicks back, when it is fired?
   A. First
   B. Second
   C. Third
   D. Gravitation

7. Which of Newton's laws explains why a car that is fully loaded takes longer to reach 100 km/h from rest than if it had no load?
   A. First
   B. Second
   C. Third
   D. Gravitation

Use the following diagram to answer the next question.

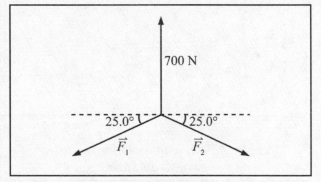

CHALLENGER QUESTION

Numerical Response

2. A motorboat travelling at a constant velocity pulls two water-skiers behind it. Each rope makes an angle of 25.0° with respect to the back of the boat. If the boat exerts a force of 700 N, the tension in each rope is _____ N. (Record your answer as a **three-digit** number.)

Use the following information to answer the next question.

The diagram below illustrates weights of equal mass hanging from strings of similar length.

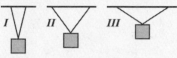

8. Which diagram shows the weight placing the **most** tension on its strings?

A. *I*

B. *II*

C. *III*

D. The tension is equal in each diagram.

Numerical Response

3. A small boy pulls his 20 kg wagon, accelerating it at 1.5 m/s². There is a force of friction of 5.0 N opposing him, and the handle of the wagon makes an angle of 45° to the ground. The force the boy exerts along the handle is _____ N. (Record your answer as a **two-digit** number.)

CHALLENGER QUESTION

9. Two children on a toboggan slide down a snow-covered hill at a slope of 35°. The total mass of the children and the toboggan is 65 kg. The coefficient of friction is 0.18. If the children start at rest, how fast are they going after 6.0 s?

A. 18 m/s   B. 25 m/s

C. 39 m/s   D. 47 m/s

10. A 110 kg person is standing in an elevator. As the elevator starts, a scale records the person's weight. In order for the scale to show the person's weight as 1 000 N, the elevator must accelerate at a rate of

A. 9.09 m/s² upward

B. 0.719 m/s² upward

C. 9.09 m/s² downward

D. 0.719 m/s² downward

Use the following information to answer the next two questions.

A wooden crate with a mass of 20.0 kg is dragged across a floor at a constant speed by a force of 85.0 N.

Numerical Response

4. The magnitude of the force of friction is _____ N. (Record your answer as a **three-digit** number.)

5. The coefficient of kinetic friction is $a.bc \times 10^{-d}$. The value of *abcd* is _____. (Record your answer as a **four-digit** number.)

Use the following information to answer the next question.

Lenny and Kyle measured the force needed to pull a block of wood across the tile floor in their classroom in two trials. In the first trial, they pulled the block across the floor when the floor was dirty. Then they cleaned and waxed the floor before their second trial. Lenny and Kyle observed that the normal force __*i*__ and the coefficient of friction __*ii*__

11. Which of the following rows correctly completes the given statement?

	i	*ii*
A.	changed	changed
B.	changed	stayed the same
C.	stayed the same	changed
D.	stayed the same	stayed the same

12. The coefficient of static friction between a desk and a calculator is 1.3. The mass of the calculator is 120 g. The force needed to slide the calculator is

A. 0.16 N

B. 1.5 N

C. 0.16 kN

D. 1.5 kN

13. Fred has a mass of 65 kg and is riding in an elevator. He feels a sensation of weighing 700 N. The acceleration of the elevator is

A. 0.96 m/s² upward

B. 0.96 m/s² downward

C. 10.8 m/s² upward

D. 10.8 m/s² downward

Numerical Response

6. While running an obstacle course, Jane comes to a rope hanging from a platform. She grabs a rope, which then accelerates her up into the air. Her mass is 55.0 kg, and she accelerates upward at 1.50 m/s². The tension in the rope is _____ N. (Record your answer to three significant digits.)

Use the following information to answer the next question.

Sam kicks a 2.3-kg textbook across the floor of his classroom. The book's initial speed is 2.1 m/s to the right, and it slides 1.6 m before coming to rest.

$\vec{v}_i = 2.1$ m/s

CHALLENGER QUESTION

14. Which free-body diagram represents the forces acting on the books after it was kicked?

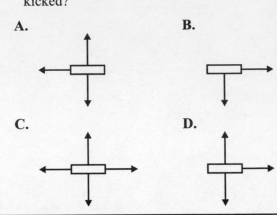

A.

B.

C.

D.

Use the following information to answer the next question.

A loaded cart with a mass of 100 kg is pulled by a force of 500 N.

15. If the cart is accelerating at 1.50 m/s², what is the magnitude of the force of friction on the cart?

A. 150 N

B. 350 N

C. 500 N

D. 850 N

16. A woman has a mass of 66.0 kg on Earth. How much does she weigh in newtons?

A. 110 N

B. 145 N

C. 647 N

D. 660 N

17. Isaac Newton's law of universal gravitation is a mathematical law best illustrated by

A. $F \propto \dfrac{1}{r^2}$

B. $T^2 \propto r^3$

C. $\vec{F} \propto \vec{a}$

D. $G = $ constant

Use the following information to answer the next question.

The purpose of Henry Cavendish's experiment was to test Newton's law of universal gravitation.

---

18. The key part of the design of this experiment was
    A. a vertical spring with an oscillating mass
    B. lead spheres rolling down an inclined plane
    C. lead spheres dropped from different heights
    D. a torsion balance with a lead sphere on each end

Use the following information to answer the next question.

There is considerable interest and some controversy about the possible existence of life on Mars. Mars has a mass of 6.42×10^{23} and a radius of 3 380 km.

Numerical Response

7. When a probe or manned mission is sent to Mars, the local value of the acceleration due to gravity is expected to be _____ m/s^2. (Record your answer to **three** significant digits.)

Use the following information to answer the next three questions.

Jupiter is the largest planet in the solar system. It has a mass of 1.90×10^{27} kg and a radius of 7.18×10^7 m.

---

19. What is the acceleration due to gravity of an object near Jupiter's surface?
    A. 4.07 m/s^2
    B. 14.7 m/s^2
    C. 17.7 m/s^2
    D. 24.6 m/s^2

Use your recorded answer from the multiple choice question 19 to answer the numerical response question 8. *

CHALLENGER QUESTION

Numerical Response

8. A person who weighs 900 N on Earth would weigh _____ kN on Jupiter. (Record your answer to **three** significant digits.)
*(You may receive marks for this question even if the previous question is answered incorrectly.)

---

20. If a person has a mass of 45.0 kg on Earth, on Jupiter that person would weigh
    A. 1.11×10^2 kg
    B. 1.11×10^3 N
    C. 1.81×10^2 kg
    D. 1.81×10^3 N

Use the following information to answer the next question.

Often, when you are shown pictures of astronauts floating around inside a space shuttle, you are told that they are "weightless." In fact, at 400 km above Earth, they are still within the gravitational field of Earth.

Numerical Response

9. The gravitational field strength at 400 km above Earth's surface is _____ N/kg. (Record your answer to **three** significant digits.)

21. The mass of the sun is 1.98×10^{30} kg and Earth orbits the sun at a distance of 1.50×10^{11} m. The force of gravity between Earth and the sun is
    A. 3.51×10^{22} N
    B. 5.27×10^{33} N
    C. 5.87×10^{-3} N
    D. 1.77×10^{-8} N

Written Response

1. Fred left his 1 850 kg car in neutral when he parked it on his driveway. The driveway is angled 7.0° from the horizontal, and the force of friction is 950 N.

a) Draw a free-body diagram for this situation.

b) Find the components of the force of gravity perpendicular and parallel to the driveway.

c) Find the acceleration of the car.

2. The coefficient of kinetic friction between a block and an inclined plane is 0.420. The angle of inclination of the plane with respect to the horizontal is set and the block is pushed down the plane. If the block moves with constant velocity after being pushed, what is the angle between the block and the plane?

ANSWERS AND SOLUTIONS—PRACTICE QUESTIONS

1. A	7. B	NR5. 4331	16. C	NR9. 8.70
2. C	NR2. 828	11. C	17. A	21. A
NR1. 10	8. C	12. B	18. D	WR1. See Solution
3. B	NR3. 49	13. A	NR7. 3.75	WR2. See Solution
4. D	9. B	NR6. 622	19. D	
5. A	10. D	14. A	NR8. 2.26	
6. C	NR4. 85.0	15. B	20. B	

1. A

Since the forces are directly opposed to each other, the body will accelerate in the direction of the greater force.

If the forces are equal, the velocity of the body should be constant (Newton's first law). The body is slowing down, which means that it is accelerating in the direction of $\vec{F}_1$.

Therefore, $\vec{F}_1 > \vec{F}_2$.

2. C

Newton's first law states that an object at rest tends to stay at rest. In order to make an object move, you must overcome its inertia. Once in motion, the object's mass (inertia) tends to stay in motion, so it is easier to move.

NR 1   10

$$\vec{F}_{net} = m\vec{a}$$
$$= (5\ 200\ \text{kg})(2.0\ \text{m/s}^2)$$
$$= 1.0 \times 10^4\ \text{N}$$
$$= 10\ \text{kN}$$

3. B

$$\vec{F}_g = m\vec{g} = \left(\frac{150\ \text{kg}}{3}\right)(9.81\ \text{N/kg})$$
$$= 491\ \text{N}$$

4. D

The principle, stated generally, is that for every action there is an equal and opposite reaction (Newton's third law).

5. A

The passenger going through the windshield is an example of Newton's first law, which states that a body in motion prefers to stay in motion unless acted upon by an unbalanced force.

6. C

The recoil of the rifle is an example of Newton's third law, which states that for every action force, there is an equal but opposite (in direction) reaction force.

7. B

Newton's second law explains why a fully loaded car takes longer to accelerate than when empty. This is because the acceleration produced by a force on the car is directly proportional to the force and inversely proportional to the mass of the car.

$$\vec{a} = \frac{\vec{F}}{m}$$

NR 2   828

$\vec{F}_{net} = 0$ because $\vec{a} = 0$ (constant velocity).

The components of $\vec{F}_1$ and $\vec{F}_2$ parallel to the back of the boat have equal magnitudes. Therefore, from the Pythagorean theorem, the magnitude of $\vec{F}_1$ is equal to the magnitude of $\vec{F}_2$.

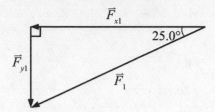

The vertical components must add up to 700 N.
$$F_1 \sin 25.0° + F_2 \sin 25.0° = 700 \text{ N}$$
$$2F_1 \sin 25.0° = 700 \text{ N}$$
$$F_1 = \frac{350 \text{ N}}{\sin 25.0°}$$
$$F_1 = 828 \text{ N}$$
$$F_2 = F_1 = 828 \text{ N}$$

The y-component (vertical) is calculated using $\sin 25.0°$ in this case.

8.   C

Since the mass is not moving, the vertical components of the tension force in the strings are equal to the weight of the object.

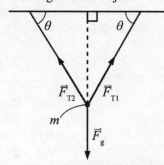

The symmetry in the given diagram means that $F_{T1} = F_{T2}$. To balance the force of gravity, the vertical components of the tension forces must add up to F_g.
$$F_{T1y} + F_{T2y} = F_g$$
$$F_{T1} \sin \theta + F_{T2} \sin \theta = F_g$$
$$2F_{T1} \sin \theta = F_g$$
$$F_{T1} = F_{T2} = \frac{F_g}{2 \sin \theta}$$

As θ increases, $\sin\theta$ increases. Therefore, both F_{T1} and F_{T2} will decrease. Therefore, the scenario where θ is smallest will have the largest tension force in the string. Therefore, diagram *III* shows the weight placing the most tension on its strings.

NR 3   49

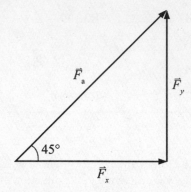

$$\vec{F}_{net} = m\vec{a}$$
$$= (20 \text{ kg})(1.5 \text{ m/s}^2)$$
$$= 30 \text{ N}$$

$\vec{F}_x$ is responsible for the wagon's horizontal motion. Therefore, the x-component of the applied force $\vec{F}_a$ is part of the net force. Since the object is not moving vertically, $\vec{F}_y$ is not needed.

$$\vec{F}_{net} = \vec{F}_x + \vec{F}_F$$
$$30 \text{ N} = F_a (\cos 45°) + (-5.0 \text{ N})$$
$$F_a = \frac{35 \text{ N}}{\cos 45°}$$
$$F_a = 49 \text{ N}$$

9.   B

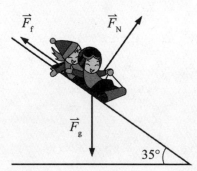

$$\vec{F}_{net\,x} = \vec{F}_{gx} + \vec{F}_f$$
$$F_{net\,x} = F_{gx} - F_f$$
$$ma_x = mg(\sin \theta) - \mu F_N$$
$$ma_x = mg(\sin \theta) - \mu mg(\cos \theta)$$

Calculate the magnitude of acceleration down the hill.

$$a_x = g\big((\sin\theta) - \mu(\cos\theta)\big)$$
$$a_x = \left(9.81 \text{ m/s}^2\right)\big((\sin 35°) - 0.18(\cos 35°)\big)$$
$$= \left(9.81 \text{ m/s}^2\right)\big(0.5736 - 0.18(0.8192)\big)$$
$$= \left(9.81 \text{ m/s}^2\right)\big(0.5736 - 0.1474\big)$$
$$= \left(9.81 \text{ m/s}^2\right)(0.426)$$
$$= 4.18 \text{ m/s}^2$$

Calculate the final speed after 6.0 s.

$$v_f = v_i + at$$
$$v_f = 0.0 + \left(4.18 \text{ m/s}^2\right)(6.0 \text{ s})$$
$$= 25 \text{ m/s}$$

10. D

The forces acting on the person are as follows:

$\vec{F}_g$ (the force of gravity on the person, i.e., his weight)

$\vec{F}_{scale}$ (the force supporting the person against the force of gravity), which in this case must be $= 1\,000$ N.

$\vec{F}_{net}$ equals the resultant (vector sum) of these two forces and equals his mass times his acceleration. In the following calculations, unless otherwise stated, positive vector quantities are upward in direction and negative quantities are downward in direction.

$$\vec{F}_{net} = \vec{F}_g + \vec{F}_{scale}$$
$$m\vec{a}_{net} = m\vec{g} + \vec{F}_{scale}$$
$$(110 \text{ kg})\vec{a} = (110 \text{ kg})(-9.81 \text{ N/kg}) + (1\,000 \text{ N})$$
$$\vec{a}_{net} = \frac{-79.1 \text{ N}}{110 \text{ kg}}$$
$$= -0.719 \text{ m/s}^2$$

The negative sign indicates that the elevator must accelerate downward, opposite to the force exerted by the scale.

Note: Be very careful to assign directions to positive and negative vector quantities and then apply them consistently.

NR 4   85.0

The crate is not accelerating, so the net force on it is zero. The magnitude of the frictional force equals the force applied to the crate.

$$F_f = F_{app}$$
$$F_f = 85.0 \text{ N}$$

NR 5   4331

You know the friction force from the previous question. The normal force is equal to the force of gravity.

$$F_f = \mu F_N$$
$$\mu = \frac{F_f}{F_N}$$
$$= \frac{85.0 \text{ N}}{20.0 \text{ kg} \times \left(9.81 \text{ m/s}^2\right)}$$
$$= 0.433$$
$$= 4.33 \times 10^{-1}$$

11. C

The normal force depends upon the mass of the wood block, which did not change. The coefficient of friction depends upon the surfaces involved so cleaning and waxing the floor will make a change.

12. B

The force needed is the force that reaches the maximum static friction force possible.

$$F_f = \mu F_N$$
$$= 1.3 \times 0.120 \text{ kg} \times 9.81 \text{ m/s}^2$$
$$= 1.5 \text{ N}$$

13. A

The upward normal force is Fred's apparent weight. His regular weight is equal to the force of gravity. The net force causes his acceleration.

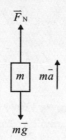

$$\vec{F}_{net} = \vec{F}_N + \vec{F}_g$$
$$m\vec{a} = \vec{F}_N + m\vec{g} \text{ so } \vec{a} = \frac{\vec{F}_N + m\vec{g}}{m}$$
$$= \frac{+700 \text{ N} + (65 \text{ kg})(-9.81 \text{ m/s}^2)}{65 \text{ kg}}$$
$$= +0.96 \text{ m/s}^2 \text{ or } 0.96 \text{ m/s}^2 \text{ upward}$$

NR 6   622

The upward tension on the rope is greater than the force of gravity on Jane. The net force causes her acceleration.

$$\vec{F}_{net} = \vec{F}_T + \vec{F}_g$$
$$\vec{F}_{net} = \vec{F}_T + m\vec{g}$$
$$\vec{F}_T = \vec{F}_{net} - m\vec{g}$$
$$= m\vec{a} - m\vec{g}$$
$$= 55.0 \text{ kg} \times 1.50 \text{ m/s}^2 - 55.0 \text{ kg} \times \left(-9.81 \text{ m/s}^2\right)$$
$$= 622 \text{ N upward}$$

14. A

Once the book has been kicked, there is no forward acting force present. There is a frictional force acting against the motion, the force due to gravity, and the normal force due to the floor pushing up on the book.

15. B

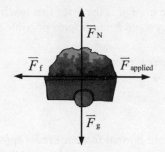

$$\vec{F}_{net} = m\vec{a}$$
$$\vec{F}_{net} = \vec{F}_{applied} + \vec{F}_f$$
$$\therefore m\vec{a} = \vec{F}_{applied} + \vec{F}_f$$
$$\vec{F}_f = m\vec{a} - \vec{F}_{applied}$$
$$= (100 \text{ kg})(1.50 \text{ m/s}^2) - 500 \text{ N}$$
$$= -350 \text{ N}$$

The force of friction is 350 N in the direction opposite to the applied force since the applied force's direction is taken to be positive.

16. C

Calculate the weight of the woman.
$$\vec{F}_g = m\vec{g}$$
$$= 66.0 \text{ kg} \times 9.81 \text{ m/s}^2$$
$$= 647 \text{ N}$$

17. A

Newton showed that elliptical orbits require that force follows an inverse square law in the formula:

$$F_g = \frac{Gm_1 m_2}{r^2}, \text{ so } F_g \propto \frac{1}{r^2}$$

18. D

In order to measure very small gravitational attractions, a very sensitive instrument like a torsion balance is required.

NR 7   3.75

$$g_{Mars} = \frac{Gm_{Mars}}{r_{Mars}^2}$$
$$= \frac{6.67 \times 10^{-11} \frac{\text{N} \cdot \text{m}^2}{\text{kg}^2} \times 6.42 \times 10^{23} \text{ kg}}{\left(3.38 \times 10^6 \text{ m}\right)^2}$$
$$= 3.75 \text{ m/s}^2$$

19. D

$$g_{Jupiter} = \frac{Gm_{Jupiter}}{r_{Jupiter}^2}$$
$$= \frac{\left(6.67 \times 10^{-11} \frac{\text{N} \cdot \text{m}^2}{\text{kg}^2}\right)\left(1.90 \times 10^{27} \text{kg}\right)}{\left(7.18 \times 10^7 \text{ m}\right)^2}$$
$$= 24.6 \text{ m/s}^2$$

This is 2.5 times that of Earth. As a result, you would "feel" very heavy on Jupiter and your body would probably collapse.

NR 8   2.26

Take the direction of the gravitational acceleration to be positive.

On Earth: $\vec{F}_{g(Earth)} = m\vec{g}$
$$900 \text{ N} = m(9.81 \text{ N/kg})$$
$$m = \frac{900 \text{ N}}{9.81 \text{ N/kg}}$$
$$= 91.7 \text{ kg}$$

On Jupiter: $\vec{F}_{g(Jupiter)} = m\vec{g}_{(Jupiter)}$

Note: Mass does not change, but weight does.

$$\vec{F}_{g(Jupiter)} = (91.7 \text{ kg})\left(24.6 \ \frac{\text{N}}{\text{kg}}\right)$$
$$= 2\ 256 \text{ N}$$
$$= 2.26 \text{ kN}$$

20. B

$$g_{\text{Jupiter}} = \frac{Gm_{\text{Jupiter}}}{r_{\text{Jupiter}}^2}$$

$$= \frac{\left(6.67 \times 10^{-11} \frac{\text{N} \cdot \text{m}^2}{\text{kg}^2}\right)\left(1.90 \times 10^{27} \text{ kg}\right)}{\left(7.18 \times 10^7 \text{ m}\right)^2}$$

$$= 24.58 \text{ m/s}^2$$

Take the direction of gravitational acceleration to be positive.

$$\vec{F}_{g(\text{Jupiter})} = m\vec{g}_{\text{Jupiter}}$$
$$= \left(45.0 \text{ kg}\right)\left(24.58 \text{ m/s}^2\right)$$
$$= 1.11 \times 10^3 \text{ N}$$

NR 9   8.70

True "weightlessness" is never really obtained. There is always some effect of other planets. The effect of the moon on your body on Earth is not a large factor because of the enormous distance between you and the moon.

$$g = \frac{Gm_E}{r^2}$$

$$= \frac{\left(6.67 \times 10^{-11} \frac{\text{N} \cdot \text{m}^2}{\text{kg}^2}\right)\left(5.98 \times 10^{24} \text{ kg}\right)}{\left(6.37 \times 10^6 \text{ m} + 4.00 \times 10^5 \text{ m}\right)^2}$$

$$= 8.70 \text{ N/kg}$$

21. A

$$F_g = \frac{Gm_1 m_2}{r^2}$$

$$= \frac{6.67 \times 10^{-11} \frac{\text{N} \cdot \text{m}^2}{\text{kg}^2}\left(5.98 \times 10^{24} \text{ kg}\right)\left(1.98 \times 10^{30} \text{ kg}\right)}{\left(1.50 \times 10^{11} \text{ m}\right)^2}$$

$$= 3.51 \times 10^{22} \text{ N}$$

---

1. **a)** *Draw a free-body diagram for this situation.*

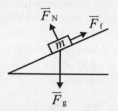

b) *Find the components of the force of gravity perpendicular and parallel to the driveway.*

$$F_{g(\perp)} = mg \cos\theta$$
$$= \left(1\ 850 \text{ kg}\right)\left(9.81 \text{ m/s}^2\right)\cos 7.0°$$
$$= 18\ 013 \text{ N}$$
$$= 18 \text{ kN}$$

$$F_{g(\parallel)} = mg \sin\theta$$
$$= \left(1\ 850 \text{ kg}\right)\left(9.81 \text{ m/s}^2\right)\sin 7.0°$$
$$= 2\ 212 \text{ N}$$
$$= 2.2 \text{ kN}$$

c) *Find the acceleration of the car.*

The car accelerates down the driveway, so the net force must also be along the driveway.
$$\vec{F}_{\text{net}} = \vec{F}_{\parallel} + \vec{F}_f$$

The frictional force acts opposite to the parallel component of the force due to gravity. So considering the magnitude of forces

$$ma = F_{\parallel} - F_f$$
$$a = \frac{F_{\parallel} - F_f}{m}$$
$$= \frac{2\ 212 \text{ N} - 950 \text{ N}}{1\ 850 \text{ kg}}$$
$$= 0.68 \text{ m/s}^2$$

The acceleration of the car is 0.68 m/s² down the driveway.

2. *The coefficient of kinetic friction between a block and an inclined plane is 0.420. The angle of inclination of the plane with respect to the horizontal is set and the block is pushed down the plane. If the block moves with constant velocity after being pushed, what is the angle between the block and the plane?*

The forces acting on the block are its weight $\vec{F}_g$, the normal force $\vec{F}_N$, and the force of kinetic friction $\vec{F}_f$, between the block and the plane. The free body diagram is as follows:

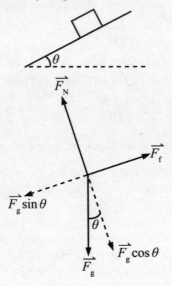

As the block moves with constant velocity, it has no acceleration. Therefore, the net force acting on it must be zero.

The perpendicular component of weight must be equal to the magnitude of the normal force.

$$F_g \cos\theta = F_N \qquad (1)$$

On the other hand, the parallel component of the weight must balance the force of kinetic friction so that there in no acceleration down the plane.

$$F_g \sin\theta = F_f = \mu_k F_N \qquad (2)$$

Divide equation (2) by equation (1).

$$\frac{F_g \sin\theta}{F_g \cos\theta} = \frac{\mu_k F_N}{F_N}$$

$$\tan\theta = \mu_k$$

$$\theta = \tan^{-1}\mu_k$$

$$= \tan^{-1}(0.420)$$

$$= 22.8°$$

UNIT TEST—DYNAMICS

CHALLENGER QUESTION

1. A driver sitting in a car pushes on the dashboard with a force of 100 N. How fast does the car accelerate, given a combined mass of 2.0×10^3 kg?

   A. 0.010 m/s^2

   B. 0.020 m/s^2

   C. 0.050 m/s^2

   D. 0 m/s^2

2. When a car moves at a constant velocity, the force the motorist applies to move the car is used to work against

   A. inertia   B. weight

   C. gravity   D. friction

Use the following information to answer the next question.

While driving along an icy road, Ellen approaches a corner. She turns the wheel to go around it, but the car continues in a straight line.

3. The law that describes this situation is

   A. Kepler's first law

   B. Newton's first law

   C. Kepler's second law

   D. Newton's second law

4. When a car stops suddenly, a passenger has a tendency to move forward. This tendency is directly related to the passenger's

   A. mass

   B. height

   C. friction

   D. position

Use the following information to answer the next question.

To make repairs to the Hubble Space Telescope, NASA astronauts used the Canadarm to grasp the telescope and bring it closer to the shuttle. When the arm applies a force on the telescope, the telescope applies a force on the arm.

5. If the two forces cancelled each other out, it would be impossible for the telescope to be moved. What is the reason that the two forces do **not** cancel each other out?

   A. The two forces act on different bodies.

   B. The two forces act in the same direction.

   C. The two forces are not equal in magnitude.

   D. Newton's laws do not apply in a vacuum.

Use the following diagram to answer the next two questions.

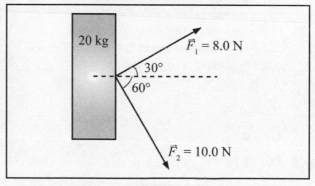

CHALLENGER QUESTION

6. Two people are trying to pull a 20 kg mass, as shown above. What is the magnitude of the net force on the mass?

   A. 2.0 N

   B. 13 N

   C. 18 N

   D. 64 N

7. The direction of the net force on the mass is
   A. 8.7° below the horizontal
   B. 21° below the horizontal
   C. 39° below the horizontal
   D. 51° below the horizontal

Use the following information to answer the next question.

The diagram to the right represents an object that has a weight of 10 N that is hung from a spring balance suspended from the roof of a stationary elevator.

Elevator

Spring balance

CHALLENGER QUESTION

8. If the elevator accelerates upward at 1.0 m/s^2, then the spring balance will show a reading closest to
   A. 0 N
   B. 9.0 N
   C. 10 N
   D. 11 N

CHALLENGER QUESTION

Numerical Response

1. A girl on a toboggan slides down a hill with a slope of 20°. The mass of the girl is 25 kg and the sled is 5.0 kg. Ignoring friction, the acceleration of the girl and sled down the hill is _____ m/s^2. (Record your answer to **two** significant digits.)

Use the following information to answer the next question.

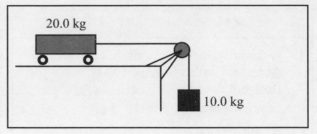

20.0 kg

10.0 kg

9. What will be the magnitude of acceleration of the cart in the above diagram? (Ignore friction and the mass of the string.)
   A. 3.27 m/s^2
   B. 4.91 m/s^2
   C. 9.81 m/s^2
   D. 19.6 m/s^2

Use the following information to answer the next question.

Stopping on in-line skates involves bringing a rubber brake pad into contact with the ground to cause friction, which eventually brings the in-line skater to a halt.

10. While Sara is in-line skating at a speed of 5.0 m/s, she sees a pothole 5.0 m ahead and immediately starts braking. What frictional force does the brake pad have to generate to stop Sara (mass of 50 kg) in a distance of 5.0 m?
    A. 63 N
    B. 10 N
    C. 0.13 kN
    D. 0.25 kN

Numerical Response

2. A picture frame weighs 12.0 N. It is hung on the wall by one wire attached to each side. The tension in each wire is equal, and the wires form an angle of 120° with each other. The tension in each wire supporting the picture frame is _____ N. (Record your answer to **three** significant digits.)

Use the following information to answer the next question.

A 110 kg football player is overweight and in danger of being cut from the team. He must reduce his weight to 1 000 N. In order to fool his coach, the player convinces him to have the weigh-in on a moving elevator.

Numerical Response

3. The football player currently weighs _____ kN. (Record your answer to **three** significant digits.)

Use the following information to answer the next question.

Sam kicks a 2.3-kg textbook across the floor of his classroom. The book's initial speed is 2.1 m/s, and it slides 1.6 m before coming to rest.

$$\vec{v}_i = 2.1 \text{ m/s}$$

Numerical Response

4. The coefficient of kinetic friction between the book and the floor is _____. (Record your answer to **two** significant digits.)

Use the following information to answer the next question.

Two forces act on an object. One force has a magnitude of 60.0 N, and it acts at 90.0° to the object's initial motion. The other force, with a magnitude of 40.0 N, acts at an angle of 180° to the object's initial motion.

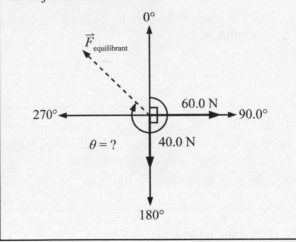

11. If a third force is exerted on the object in order to keep the object moving at its original velocity, what are the magnitude and direction of this third force?

A. 50.0 N at 137°

B. 50.0 N at 317°

C. 72.1 N at 33.7°

D. 72.1 N at 304°

12. If Earth's mass was twice its known value, the acceleration due to gravity at the surface would be

A. half its normal acceleration.

B. twice its normal acceleration.

C. equal to its normal acceleration.

D. four times its normal acceleration.

13. Which of the following quantities were obtained from the Cavendish experiment?

    A. The mass and diameter of Earth

    B. The mass of Earth and the value of G

    C. The diameter of Earth and the value of G

    D. The mass and diameter of Earth, and the value of G

Use the following information to answer the next question.

Pluto is the tenth-largest body observed directly orbiting the sun. Its acceleration due to gravity is only 6.0% of Earth's gravitational acceleration value $\left(g_{\text{Pluto}} = 0.060 g_{\text{earth}}\right)$.

14. If a woman has a mass of 50 kg on Earth, then her mass (m) and magnitude of weight (F_g) on Pluto would be

    A. $m = 50$ kg, $F_g = 29$ kg

    B. $m = 29$ kg, $F_g = 50$ kg

    C. $m = 50$ kg, $F_g = 29$ N

    D. $m = 29$ kg, $F_g = 50$ N

Numerical Response

5. The mass of a proton is 1.67×10^{-27} kg and the mass of an electron is 9.11×10^{-31} kg. A proton and an electron are 5.29×10^{-11} m apart in a hydrogen atom. The gravitational force between these particles in the hydrogen atom is $a.bc \times 10^{-de}$ N. The value of *abcde* is _____. (Record your answer as a **five-digit** number.)

15. The theoretical concept of a field was created to explain

    A. action at a distance

    B. the net force on an object

    C. the Cavendish experiment

    D. collisions between objects

ANSWERS AND SOLUTIONS—UNIT TEST

1. D	6. B	10. C	12. B
2. D	7. B	NR2. 12.0	13. B
3. B	8. D	NR3. 1.08	14. C
4. A	NR1. 3.4	NR4. 0.14	NR5. 36347
5. A	9. A	11. D	15. A

1. D

To accelerate, the force must be external. This force is internal, therefore, the car will not move. If you push on the dashboard with a force of 100 N, the dashboard pushes back on you with 100 N as well.

2. D

At a constant velocity, there is no net force, therefore, there is no acceleration. The applied force is balanced by friction.

3. B

When Ellen tries to turn, the car's momentum exceeds the frictional force between the tires and the road (reduced by the ice). As a result, the car's inertia maintains its state of motion in a straight line. This is another example of Newton's first law.

4. A

Mass is the measure of the inertia of an object. The greater the mass, the greater its inertia will be.

5. A

Newton's third law explains that for every action (force), there is an equal and opposite reaction (force). In the question, the force at work on the telescope is the "action," and the resulting force on the arm is the "reaction." Therefore, statement **C** is incorrect since the forces must be equal. Also, statement **B** is incorrect since the forces must be in opposite directions. Newton's laws are applicable in a vacuum, so statement **D** is incorrect.

Therefore, the telescope moves because the two forces act on different bodies with different masses.

6. B

Since $60° + 30° = 90°$, the Pythagorean theorem is applicable here.

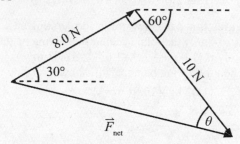

A vector diagram with vectors added tip to tail is useful. The magnitude of the net force on the mass can calculated using Pythagorean theorem

$$F_{net}{}^2 = F_1^2 + F_2^2$$
$$F_{net} = \sqrt{(8.0 \text{ N})^2 + (10 \text{ N})^2}$$
$$= 13 \text{ N}$$

7. B

$$\tan\theta = \frac{10 \text{ N}}{8.0 \text{ N}}$$
$$\theta = \tan^{-1} 1.25$$
$$\theta = 51°$$

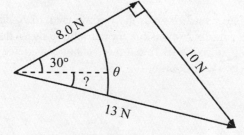

Direction of the net force on the mass is $51° - 30° = 21°$ below horizontal.

8. D

Calculate the mass of the object.

$$F_g = mg$$
$$10 \text{ N} = m(9.81 \text{ m/s}^2)$$
$$m = \frac{10 \text{ N}}{9.81 \text{ m/s}^2}$$
$$= 1.02 \text{ kg}$$

When the elevator accelerates upward the net force acting on the object is given by $\vec{F}_{net} = \vec{F}_N + \vec{F}_g$.
Use this equation to solve for the normal force.

$$\vec{F}_N = \vec{F}_{net} - \vec{F}_g$$
$$= m\vec{a} - m\vec{g}$$
$$= m(\vec{a} - \vec{g})$$
$$= (1.02 \text{ kg})[1.0 \text{ m/s}^2 - (-9.81 \text{ m/s}^2)]$$

Note: Since the elevator is accelerating upward at 1.0 m/s², the total acceleration acting on the body is (1.0 m/s² + 9.81 m/s² = 10.81 m/s²). Then the spring balance will show a reading of

$$F_N = (1.02 \text{ kg})(10.81 \text{ m/s}^2)$$
$$= 11 \text{ N}$$

NR 1   3.4

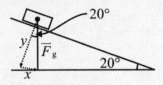

$$m_T = \text{mass of the girl} + \text{mass of the toboggan}$$
$$= (25 \text{ kg} + 5.0 \text{ kg})$$
$$= 30 \text{ kg}$$

$$F_{net} = F_{g(\parallel)} = F_g \sin \theta$$
$$m_T a = m_T g \sin \theta$$
$$(30 \text{ kg}) a = (30 \text{ kg})(9.81 \text{ N/kg}) \sin 20°$$
$$a = 3.4 \text{ m/s}^2$$

Using $\sin 20°$ gives the x-component of F_g that is entirely responsible for her motion down the hill since the frictional force is not considered when tobogganing.

9. A

The net force moving this system is the weight $(\vec{F}_g)$ of the 10 kg mass since frictional force or tension of the string is not considered.

$$F_{net} = F_g$$
$$m_\perp a = mg$$
$$(20.0 \text{ kg} + 10.0 \text{ kg}) a = (10.0 \text{ kg})(9.81 \text{ m/s}^2)$$
$$a = \frac{(10.0 \text{ kg})(9.81 \text{ m/s}^2)}{(20.0 \text{ kg} + 10.0 \text{ kg})}$$
$$= 3.27 \text{ m/s}^2$$

The magnitude of the acceleration of the cart is 3.27 m/s².

10. C

$$v_f^2 = v_i^2 + 2ad$$
$$\Rightarrow a = \frac{v_f^2 - v_i^2}{2d}$$
$$a = \frac{(0)^2 - (5.0 \text{ m/s})^2}{2(5.0 \text{ m})}$$
$$= -2.5 \text{ m/s}^2$$

Negative sign indicates that the skate is decelerating. The net force to brake the skate is equal to the frictional force.

$$\vec{F}_f = \vec{F}_{net}$$
$$\vec{F}_f = m\vec{a}$$
$$\vec{F}_f = 50 \text{ kg}(-2.5 \text{ m/s}^2)$$
$$= -125 \text{ N}$$
$$= -0.13 \text{ kN}$$

Note: The negative sign gives direction. The question only asks for magnitude, so the sign may be dropped. The frictional force generated must be 0.13 kN and acted in the direction opposite to the initial movement.

NR 2   12.0

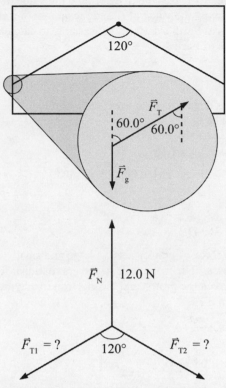

$\vec{F}_N$ | 12.0 N

$\vec{F}_{T1}$ = ?   120° $\vec{F}_{T2}$ = ?

The symmetry in the given diagram means that $F_{T1} = F_{T2}$.

The magnitude of the vertical components must add up to F_N.

$$F_{T1y} + F_{T2y} = F_N$$
$$F_{T1}\cos\theta + F_{T2}\cos\theta = F_N$$
$$2F_{T1}\cos\theta = F_N$$
$$F_{T1} = \frac{F_N}{2\cos\theta}$$
$$= \frac{12\text{ N}}{2(0.5)}$$

$\therefore F_{T1} = F_{T2} = 12$ N

The tension in each wire is 12 N.

NR 3   1.08

The football player's weight is equal to the force of gravity.

$$\vec{F}_g = m\vec{g}$$
$$= (110\text{ kg})(9.81\text{ m/s}^2)$$
$$= 1.08 \times 10^3\text{ N}$$
$$= 1.08\text{ kN}$$

NR 4   0.14

Once the book has been kicked, there is no forward force on it. There is a frictional force acting against the motion and, the net force is equal to the force of friction. This force is responsible for the acceleration of the book:

$$a = \frac{v_f^2 - v_i^2}{2d}$$
$$= \frac{0 - (2.1\text{ m/s})^2}{2(1.6\text{ m})}$$
$$a = -1.378\text{ m/s}^2$$

The negative value of a indicates that the book is decelerating.

$$\vec{F}_f = m\vec{a} = 2.3\text{ kg} \times (-1.378\text{ m/s}^2)$$
$$\vec{F}_f = -3.17\text{ N}$$

The magnitude of force of friction is 3.17 N.

$$F_f = \mu F_N$$
$$\mu = \frac{F_f}{F_N}$$
$$= \frac{(3.17\text{ N})}{2.3\text{ kg} \times (9.81\text{ m/s}^2)}$$
$$= 0.14$$

11. D

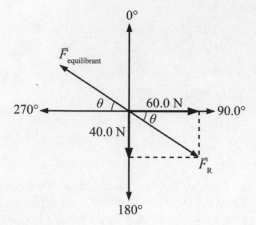

Adding the force vectors tip-to-tail gives you a right-angle triangle. The length of the hypotenuse is equal to the magnitude of the equilibrant vector, and the angle of $\theta + 270°$ (as seen above) gives you the direction relative to 0°. Find the resultant vector.

$$(F_R)^2 = (40.0 \text{ N})^2 + (60.0 \text{ N})^2$$
$$F_R = \sqrt{1\ 600 \text{ N} + 3\ 600 \text{ N}}$$
$$= 72.1 \text{ N}$$

$$\tan\theta = \frac{\text{Opposite}}{\text{Adjacent}}$$
$$\tan\theta = \frac{40 \text{ N}}{60 \text{ N}}$$
$$\theta = \tan^{-1}(0.666\ 7)$$
$$= 33.7°$$

An equilibrant force is a force that balances forces on an object. In this case, it should be equal in magnitude and opposite in direction to $\vec{F}_R$.

Since $270° + 33.7° = 303.7°$, the equilibrant vector is 72.1 N of force acting at an angle of 304°.

12. B

$$g = \frac{Gm_E}{r^2}$$

If the mass of Earth was twice its value, the acceleration due to gravity will also double, since $g \propto m_E$.

13. B

Cavendish was able to determine the value of G. Knowing the value of G and the weight of a small mass at Earth's surface, he was able to calculate the mass of Earth.

14. C

Mass does not change and the magnitude of weight is
$$F_{g(Pluto)} = mg_{Pluto}$$
$$= m(0.060g_{earth})$$
$$= (50 \text{ kg})(0.060)(9.81 \text{ m/s}^2)$$
$$= 29 \text{ N}$$

NR 5   36347

The force of gravity acts on large and small masses. The magnitude of the gravitational force between the proton and the electron in a hydrogen atom is

$$F_g = \frac{Gm_1m_2}{r^2}$$
$$= \frac{\left(6.67\times10^{-11}\ \frac{\text{N}\cdot\text{m}^2}{\text{kg}^2}\right)\times(1.67\times10^{-27}\text{ kg})(9.11\times10^{-31}\text{ kg})}{(5.29\times10^{-11}\text{ m})^2}$$
$$= 3.63\times10^{-47}\text{ N}$$

15. A

Before developing the concept of a field, scientists had difficulty explaining how two objects, not in contact, could affect each other, (i.e., action at a distance). A field is a visual method to explain gravitation causes masses to attract other masses, using field lines.

Circular Motion, Work, and Energy

CIRCULAR MOTION, WORK, AND ENERGY

Table of Correlations				
Specific Expectation	**Practice Questions**	**Unit Test Questions**	**Practice Test 1**	**Practice Test 2**
Students will:				
C1 *Explain circular motion, using Newton's laws of motion.*				
C1.1 *describe uniform circular motion as a special case of two-dimensional motion*	8			
C1.2 *explain, qualitatively and quantitatively, that the acceleration in uniform circular motion is directed toward the centre of a circle*	5	1	24	17, NR10
C1.3 *explain, quantitatively, the relationships among speed, frequency, period, and radius for circular motion*	1, 2, 7, 11, NR3	3, WR1	NR7, 23	21, 27
C1.4 *explain, qualitatively, uniform circular motion in terms of Newton's laws of motion*		4	22, 25	18
C1.5 *explain, quantitatively, planetary and natural and artificial satellite motion, using circular motion to approximate elliptical orbits*	3, 4, NR1, 6	2, 5	NR9	
C1.6 *predict the mass of a celestial body from the orbital data of a satellite in uniform circular motion around the celestial body*	9, 10	NR1	WR1	NR11
C1.7 *explain, qualitatively, how Kepler's laws were used in the development of Newton's law of universal gravitation*	NR2	6	26	
C2 *Explain that work is a transfer of energy and that conservation of energy in an isolated system is a fundamental physical concept.*				
C2.1 *define mechanical energy as the sum of kinetic and potential energy*	12, 15	14, 15	NR8	NR9
C2.2 *determine, quantitatively, the relationships among the kinetic, gravitational potential, and total mechanical energies of a mass at any point between maximum potential energy and maximum kinetic energy*	NR5, 17	12, 13	21	16
C2.3 *analyze, quantitatively, kinematics and dynamics problems that relate to the conservation of mechanical energy in an isolated system*	NR6, 18, 19	8, 10, 11		26, NR14
C2.4 *recall work as a measure of the mechanical energy transferred and power as the rate of doing work*	13, 14, NR7	NR2	20	24
C2.5 *describe power qualitatively and quantitatively*	NR4	7, NR3	19	25
C2.6 *describe, qualitatively, the change in mechanical energy in a system that is not isolated*	16	9		

CIRCULAR MOTION, WORK, AND ENERGY

C1.1   describe uniform circular motion as a special case of two-dimensional motion

C1.2   explain, qualitatively and quantitatively, that the acceleration in uniform circular motion is directed toward the centre of a circle

UNIFORM CIRCULAR MOTION

Newton's first law, an object stays in motion unless acted upon by an outside force, demonstrates an object's tendency to continue moving in a defined way. In circular motion, the direction of motion is always changing in both horizontal and vertical components. Therefore, an object moving in a circle is accelerating continually, even if its speed is not changing. This acceleration is called centripetal acceleration $(\vec{a}_c)$.

The direction of the acceleration is toward the centre of the circle. The term centripetal means "directed toward the centre." When a force acts on an object at right angles to the object's velocity, and that force remains at right angles to that velocity, the object will move in a circle. The force is always directed toward the centre of the circle, and is therefore a centripetal force $(\vec{F}_c)$.

The magnitude of the centripetal acceleration is found with the formula: $a_c = \dfrac{v^2}{r}$. No vector arrows appear in this formula, on a_c or v as their magnitudes are considered only.

Example

Find the centripetal acceleration of a car turning in a circle with a radius of 12 m and at a speed of 10 m/s.

$$a_c = \frac{v^2}{r}$$
$$= \frac{(10 \text{ m/s})^2}{12 \text{ m}}$$
$$= 8.3 \text{ m/s}^2$$

Practice Questions: 5, 8

C1.3   explain, quantitatively, the relationships among speed, frequency, period and radius for circular motion

IMPORTANT VARIABLES FOR UNIFORM CIRCULAR MOTION

Sometimes when analyzing circular motion the speed is not known. Instead, the period of time it takes to go around the circle once is known. This period of time is known as the period (T) of the circular motion. Remember that speed is distance divided by time. Applying this to circular motion, the following formulas can be developed:

$$v = \frac{d}{t} \qquad\qquad a_c = \frac{4\pi^2 r}{T^2}$$
$$= \frac{2\pi r}{T}$$

In circular motion, you also discuss frequency (f), the number of revolutions per second.

$$f = \frac{1}{T} \quad \text{or} \quad T = \frac{1}{f}$$

Example

A person swings a ball on the end of 40-cm long string. Given that the period of revolution is $\frac{1}{3}$ s per revolution, find the frequency and velocity of its motion.

$$T = \frac{1}{f} \qquad\qquad v = \frac{2\pi r}{T}$$
$$f = \frac{1}{T} \qquad\qquad = \frac{2\pi(0.40 \text{ cm})}{\frac{1}{3}\text{s}}$$
$$= \frac{1}{\frac{1}{3}\text{s}} \qquad\qquad = 7.5 \text{ m/s}$$
$$= 3.0 \text{ s}^{-1}$$
$$= 3.0 \text{ Hz}$$

The unit for revolution per second is called a hertz (Hz) which is equivalent to inverse seconds (s^{-1}).

Example

A yo-yo swings on the end of a string. The frequency of the circular motion is 4.00 Hz, and the radius of the motion is 0.800 m. Find the centripetal acceleration of the yo-yo.

$$T = \frac{1}{f}$$
$$= \frac{1}{4.00 \text{ Hz}}$$
$$= 0.250 \text{ s}$$
$$a_c = \frac{4\pi^2 r}{T^2}$$
$$= \frac{4\pi^2 (0.800 \text{ m})}{(0.250 \text{ s})^2}$$
$$= 505 \text{ m/s}^2$$

Practice Questions: 1, 2, 7, 11, NR3

C1.4 explain, qualitatively, uniform circular motion in terms of Newton's laws of motion

UNIFORM CIRCULAR MOTION AND NEWTON'S LAWS

It is important to note that centripetal force is not a type of force but rather a direction of force. Many types of forces can be centripetal in certain situations.

Gravitational forces always act downward, thus affecting the vertical component of an object's motion. When an object moves in a vertical circle, gravity, or some component of gravity, is part of the net centripetal force.

Normal forces are often centripetal. In the case of a roller coaster in a vertical loop, the normal force from the rails is part of the net centripetal force.

Friction forces are often centripetal. When a car turns, the friction force from the road surface pushes the car toward the centre of the circle.

Tension forces are centripetal when things are swinging in circles attached to strings or ropes.

Example

Identify the centripetal forces in each following situation.

a)

The forces are the tension in the string minus gravity when the bob is at the bottom of the circle and tension plus gravity when the bob is at the top of the circular path.

b) A car turns a corner.

HORIZONTAL CIRCLES

Example

Find the centripetal force required to keep a 1 000 kg car moving in a uniform circle of radius 50.0 m at a speed of 50.0 km/h.

Convert the units from km/h to m/s.

$$50.0 \text{ km/h} = \left(\frac{50.0 \text{ km}}{1.00 \text{ h}}\right)\left(\frac{1 000 \text{ m}}{1.00 \text{ km}}\right)\left(\frac{1.00 \text{ h}}{3 600 \text{ s}}\right)$$
$$= 13.89 \text{ m/s}$$

Calculate the magnitude of the centripetal force.
$$F_c = ma_c$$
$$F_c = m\frac{v^2}{r}$$
$$= (1 000 \text{ kg})\frac{(13.89 \text{ m/s})^2}{50.0 \text{ m}}$$
$$= 3.86 \times 10^3 \text{ N}$$

Example

The centripetal force required to keep a 400 kg motorbike moving in a uniform circular path of radius 75.0 m is 4 000 N. What is the speed of the motorbike, in km/h?

$$F_c = m\frac{v^2}{r}$$

$$4\ 000\ \text{N} = (400\ \text{kg})\left(\frac{v^2}{75.0\ \text{m}}\right)$$

$$v^2 = 750\ \text{m}^2/\text{s}^2$$

$$v = 27.4\ \text{m/s}$$

$$= \left(\frac{27.4\ \cancel{m}}{1.00\ \cancel{s}}\right)\left(\frac{3\ 600\ \cancel{s}}{1.00\ \text{h}}\right)\left(\frac{1.00\ \text{km}}{1\ 000\ \cancel{m}}\right)$$

$$= 98.6\ \text{km/h}$$

Example

A person swings a 100 g ball in a horizontal circle at the end of a 55.0 cm string. The string makes 2.50 revolutions in 1.00 s. Find the magnitude of the centripetal force.

The net force on the ball must be non-zero. It must be significant to alter the ball's path in a continuous, circular path. In this case, the centripetal force is the tension in the string.

$$T = \frac{1}{f} \qquad\qquad v = \frac{2\pi r}{T}$$

$$= \frac{1}{2.50\ \text{s}^{-1}} \qquad = \frac{2\pi(0.550\ \text{m})}{0.400\ \text{s}}$$

$$= 0.400\ \text{s} \qquad = 8.639\ \text{m/s}$$

$$F_T = F_c = \frac{mv^2}{r}$$

$$= \frac{(0.100\ \text{kg})(8.639\ \text{m/s})^2}{0.550\ \text{m}}$$

$$F_c = 13.6\ \text{N}$$

Another approach to this question is to use the formula for centripetal acceleration in terms of the period.

$$F_c = ma_c$$

$$= m\frac{4\pi^2 r}{T^2}$$

$$= (0.100\ \text{kg})\left(\frac{4(3.14^2)(0.55\ \text{m})}{(0.400\ \text{s})^2}\right)$$

$$= 13.6\ \text{N}$$

VERTICAL CIRCLES

Example

A person swings the same ball (mass = 0.100 kg) in a vertical circle at the end of a 55.0 cm string. The string makes 2.50 revolutions in one second. Find the string tension at both the upper and lower ends of its arc.

a) Make a free-body diagram for the ball at the top of the circle:

The acceleration is toward the centre of the circle (below the ball). The net force is the sum of the two forces.

$$\vec{F}_T + \vec{F}_g = \vec{F}_{net} = \vec{F}_c$$

Determine the period of one revolution.

$$T = \frac{1}{f}$$

$$= \frac{1}{2.50\ \text{s}^{-1}}$$

$$= 0.400\ \text{s}$$

Calculate the magnitude of the forces.

$$F_T + F_g = F_{net}$$

$$F_T + mg = \frac{4\pi^2 mr}{T^2}$$

$$\Rightarrow F_T = \frac{4\pi^2 mr}{T^2} - mg$$

$$F_T = \left(\frac{4\pi^2(0.100\ \text{kg})(0.550\ \text{m})}{(0.400\ \text{s})^2}\right)$$

$$\qquad\quad - 0.100\ \text{kg} \times 9.81\ \text{m/s}^2$$

$$F_T = 12.6\ \text{N}$$

b) Now, do the same at the bottom of the circle.

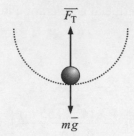

The net acceleration is toward the centre of the circle (above the ball). The tension is directed towards the centre of the circular path whereas weight is directed opposite to it. The tension must be larger than the gravitational force. The magnitude of the net force is the difference of the two forces.

$$\vec{F}_T - \vec{F}_g = \vec{F}_{net} = \vec{F}_c$$

$$F_T - F_g = F_{net}$$

$$F_T - mg = \frac{4\pi^2 mr}{T^2}$$

$$\Rightarrow F_T = \frac{4\pi^2 mr}{T^2} + mg$$

$$F_T = \left(\frac{4\pi^2 (0.100 \text{ kg})(0.550 \text{ m})}{(0.400 \text{ s})^2} \right)$$
$$+ 0.100 \text{ kg} \times 9.81 \text{ m/s}^2$$

$$F_T = 14.5 \text{ N}$$

C1.5   *explain, quantitatively, planetary and natural and artificial satellite motion, using circular motion to approximate elliptical orbits*

C1.6   *predict the mass of a celestial body from the orbital data of a satellite in uniform circular motion around the celestial body*

SATELLITE MOTION

In circular motion, acceleration is directed towards the centre of the circle. This must also be true for celestial bodies, such as Earth and the moon. Even though no physical tie exists between the two, gravity is the force keeping them together.

Isaac Newton worked out mathematically the shapes of the planets' orbits by assuming that the force of gravity was acting as the centripetal force. Although planetary orbits are elliptical, they are extremely close to perfect circles. Algebraically, Newton's argument is: $\vec{F}_g = \vec{F}_c = m\vec{a}_c$.

Depending upon whether the speed of a satellite, moon, or planet in its orbit is known, or whether the period of its orbit is known, the algebra takes on this form:

$$F_g = ma_c$$

$$\frac{Gm_1 m_2}{r^2} = \frac{m_2 v^2}{r}$$

or

$$\frac{Gm_1 m_2}{r^2} = \frac{4\pi^2 m_2 r}{T^2}$$

Example

Find the speed of Jupiter's moon, Io, in its orbit. The orbital radius is 4.22×10^8 m and the mass of Jupiter is 1.90×10^{27} kg.

$$F_g = ma_c$$

$$\frac{Gm_{\text{Jupiter}} m_{\text{Io}}}{r^2} = \frac{m_{\text{Io}} v^2}{r}$$

Notice that the mass of Io is on both sides of the equation. This can be divided out of the equation. This is true for all orbit calculations—the mass of the body in orbit cancels out. As well, the radius cancels out on the right side of the equation.

As a result, the equation becomes $\dfrac{Gm_{\text{Jupiter}}}{r} = v^2$.

Therefore, solving for the speed of Io's orbit is as follows:

$$v = \sqrt{\dfrac{Gm_{\text{Jupiter}}}{r}}$$
$$= \sqrt{\dfrac{\left(6.67\times10^{-11}\ \text{N}\cdot\text{m}^2/\text{kg}^2\right)\left(1.90\times10^{27}\ \text{kg}\right)}{4.22\times10^8\ \text{m}}}$$
$$= 1.73\times10^4\ \text{m/s}$$
$$= 17.3\ \text{km/s}$$

Example

Find the speed of a space station in its orbit 360 km above Earth.

To answer this question, you need the orbital radius. The radius of Earth is 6 370 km $(6.37\times10^6\ \text{m})$ and the space station is 360 km above the ground. Thus, its radius of orbit is 6 730 km, or 6.73×10^6 m.

$$\dfrac{Gm_{\text{E}}m_{\text{ss}}}{r^2} = \dfrac{m_{\text{ss}}v^2}{r}$$
$$v = \sqrt{\dfrac{Gm_{\text{E}}}{r}}$$
$$= \sqrt{\dfrac{\left(6.67\times10^{-11}\ \text{N}\cdot\text{m}^2/\text{kg}^2\right)\left(5.98\times10^{24}\ \text{kg}\right)}{6.73\times10^6\ \text{m}}}$$
$$= 7\ 698\ \text{m/s}$$
$$= 7.70\ \text{km/s}$$

Practice Questions: 3, 4, NR1, 6, 9, 10

C1.7   explain, qualitatively, how Kepler's laws were used in the development of Newton's law of universal gravitation

KEPLER'S LAWS OF PLANETARY MOTION

Kepler came up with three laws of planetary motion in the 1600s.

First law: the planets travel in ellipses around the sun.

Second law: the planets move faster when they are close to the sun, and slower when they are farther away from the sun.

Third law: for all the planets, the value of $\dfrac{r^3}{T^2}$ is a constant.

Johannes Kepler developed these laws but he did not explain how they worked. It was Newton's law of universal gravitational that eventually explained why they worked. Kepler's second law can also be stated as follows: as satellites orbit around the more massive object, they sweep out an equal area in the ellipse in an equal amount of time. Kepler's third law can be used as a shortcut for answering some questions.

Example

Mars is 1.52 times farther from the sun than Earth. What is Mars' orbital period?

Since $\dfrac{r^3}{T^2}$ is constant, it is the same for Earth and Mars. Therefore,

$$\dfrac{r_{\text{M}}^3}{T_{\text{M}}^2} = \dfrac{r_{\text{E}}^3}{T_{\text{E}}^2} \Rightarrow T_{\text{M}} = \sqrt{\dfrac{r_{\text{M}}^3 T_{\text{E}}^2}{r_{\text{E}}^3}}$$
$$T_{\text{M}} = \sqrt{\dfrac{\left(1.52\ \text{AU}\right)^3 \left(365.25\ \text{d}\right)^2}{\left(1\ \text{AU}\right)^3}}$$
$$T_{\text{M}} = 684\ \text{d}$$

Since this is a comparison of two ratios, you can use any units you want for the radii and periods of the planets.

Practice Question: NR2

C2.1   define mechanical energy as the sum of kinetic and potential energy

MECHANICAL ENERGY

The mechanical energy for a system of objects is the sum of all the potential energy (due to gravity or the mechanical compression of a material) and all the kinetic energy of the objects in the system. Energy is a scalar quantity but there are situations where a negative potential energy makes sense. This negative does not however represent a negative direction. The kinetic energy of an object is proportional to the square of its speed. Kinetic energy is defined as:

$$E_{kinetic} = \frac{1}{2}mv^2.$$

Potential energy is related to position relative to a reference point. In the case of gravitational potential energy, the amount of energy is proportional to the distance or height above to reference point, usually taken to be the surface of Earth.

$$E_{potential} = mgh$$

The choice of reference point is arbitrary. In the case of potential energy, a negative potential energy simply means that some energy is required to move that object to a location where it possesses no potential energy.

Example

A 2 000 kg plane is flying 500 m above the ground at a velocity of 30.0 m/s. What is the plane's total mechanical energy?

$$E_{mechanical} = E_{potential} + E_{kinetic}$$
$$= mgh + \frac{1}{2}mv^2$$
$$= (2\ 000 \text{ kg})(9.81 \text{ m/s}^2)(500 \text{ m})$$
$$+ \frac{1}{2}(2\ 000 \text{ kg})(30.0 \text{ m/s})^2$$
$$= 9.81 \text{ MJ} + 0.900 \text{ MJ}$$
$$E_{mechanical} = 10.7 \text{ MJ}$$

Practice Questions: 12, 15

C2.2   determine, quantitatively, the relationships among the kinetic, gravitational potential and total mechanical energies of a mass at any point between maximum potential energy and maximum kinetic energy

CONSERVATION OF MECHANICAL ENERGY

Suppose that a ball is thrown upward and then caught. The ball has a combination of kinetic and gravitational potential energy at all points of its trajectory. Ignoring friction, you will notice that one kind of energy changes to another, while the total energy is constant. This can be shown graphically:

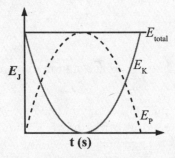

In the graph, the potential and kinetic energies change from one to the other, and the total mechanical energy remains constant throughout.

According to previous discussion energy is a scalar quantity. This means that it does not have direction, only magnitude. The actual energy of a system is neither negative nor positive. Instead, only the change in energy has a negative or positive value. An energy change is positive when the system gains energy, and it is negative when it has lost energy.

Practice Questions: NR5, 17

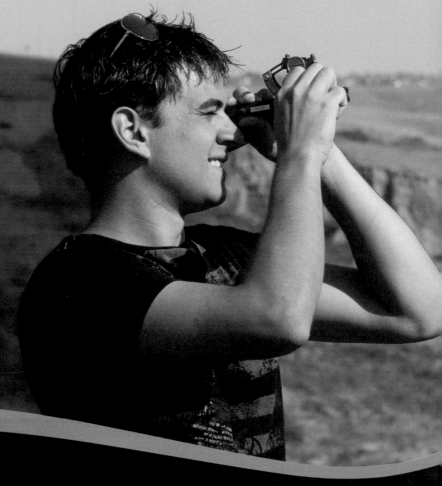

LOOK TO Lethbridge College

Lethbridge College gives students the tools they need to connect to the work they'll love.
During their two years of study, students are fully immersed in one of more than 50 career-training programs – from criminal justice to multimedia design to environmental science to engineering. They quickly start to practice the concepts they're learning in the classroom. They get to engage in applied research – finding practical solutions to real world problems. And Lethbridge College graduates are a welcome addition to any workplace – because they're equipped with experience and ready to go on day one.

Look to Lethbridge College.
Welcome to Your Future.

Lethbridge College

lethbridgecollege.ca

ROTARY
NEW GENERATIONS

Under 30 years of age and making a difference at home and abroad

RYLA (Rotary Youth Leadership Awards) is an exciting program for youth who have potential to be leaders today and tomorrow. RYLA emphasizes leadership, citizenship, and personal growth.

INTERACT is a service club for young people ages 14 to 18. Interact has lots of fun activities, but there is also a serious side that appeals to thousands of youth. Excellent opportunities for service!

RYPEN (Rotary Youth Program of Enrichment) is a four-day camp designed for young people who want to grow. RYPEN camps are for youth who have limited opportunities to attend leadership development programs.

ROTARACT is a Rotary service program for young men and women ages 18 to 30. ROTARACT is one of Rotary's fastest-growing programs. ROTARACT is about making a difference through service.

ROTARY YOUTH EXCHANGE students spend up to a year living with host families and attending school in a different country. Youth Exchange Students learn new ways of living and new things about themselves.

ROTARY INTERNATIONAL is a world-wide organization committed to service, high ethical standards and promoting peace throughout the world. Rotary International supports a variety of global youth initiatives.

For more information:

Northern Alberta BC, Saskatchewan	www.Rotary5370.org/youth
Southern Alberta & Saskatchewan	www.rotaryyouth.com

Sponsored by

OVERWHELMED?

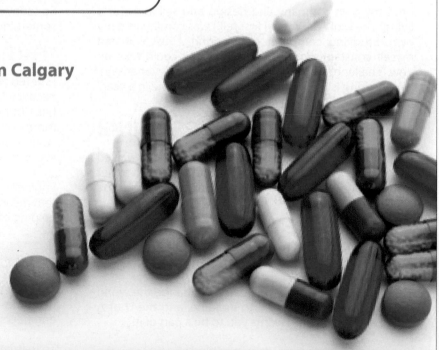

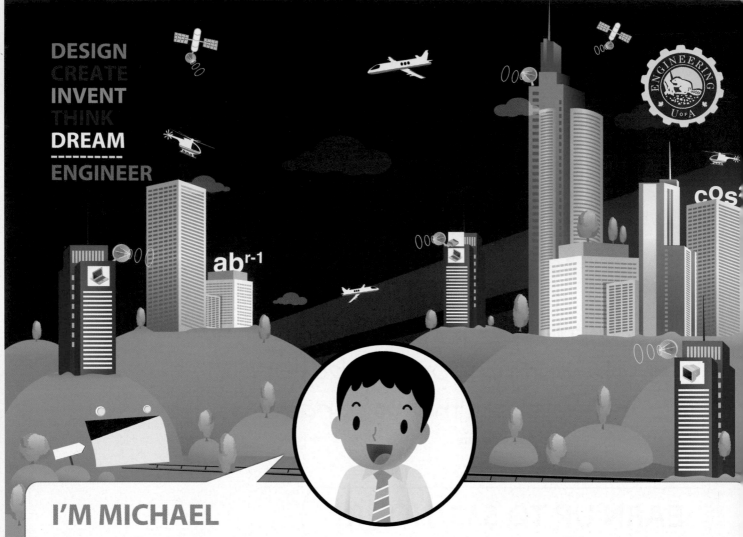

**DESIGN
CREATE
INVENT
THINK
DREAM
————————
ENGINEER**

ab^{r-1}

$\cos^2$

I'M MICHAEL

I run my own company and design and sell apps for a living! The U of A is where I first felt I was coming into my own. Studying computer engineering, I just watched myself constantly grow. I learned that I could take on new challenges and do new things. Everyone says, 'Engineering is really hard,' and, 'You'll be gone in a year.' But the truth is that you just

START GROWING AND GROWING!

Eventually, I got this feeling that any time I walked toward a new challenge, I knew it might be tough to get through but whatever was on the other side would be awesome.

So today, when I see a problem that looks really thorny, something maybe you'd rather avoid, I look at it and say

'THIS IS GONNA BE AWESOME!'

I started my first company a few months after graduating because I really wanted to run my own business. It was hard, but I've gotten better at that, too. I've started a few more companies and I like working with students who want to start their own companies too, so they can be as successful as possible!

Engineers are just like artists—they're creative. For me, that means building apps and building companies—and helping other people along the way.

The next generation of engineers will change the world in ways we can only begin to imagine, and the U of A Faculty of Engineering wants you to be a part of it!

The things you use every day—the iPod you listen to, the cell phone you text with, even the systems that provide you with clean drinking water—have all been designed and built by engineers. Things you will use in the future—eco-friendly energy sources, innovative

medical technology and revolutionary social media networks—will be the products of tomorrow's creative engineers. You could be one of them!

To learn more about engineering, please visit:
www.engineering.ualberta.ca

**FACULTY OF
ENGINEERING**
UNIVERSITY OF ALBERTA

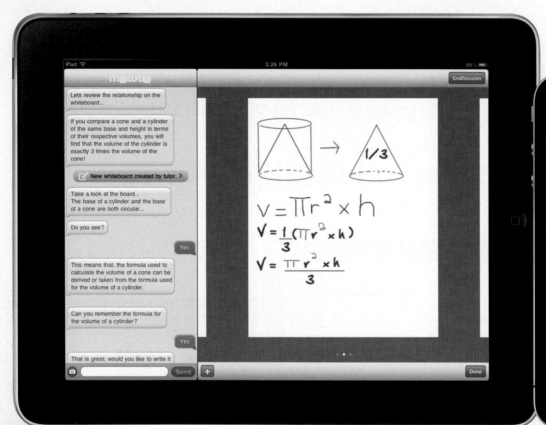

*C2.3   analyze, quantitatively, kinematics
and dynamics problems that relate
to the conservation of mechanical energy
in an isolated system*

CONSERVATION OF MECHANICAL ENERGY IN AN ISOLATED SYSTEM

The first law of thermodynamics states that energy cannot be created or destroyed, but only transformed from one state to another. This law can be tested using algebraic or graphical analysis of mechanical systems.

Algebraic analysis is based on mathematical relationships that exist between mass, time, distance, velocity, force, and energy, such that
$$\Sigma E_{\text{initial}} = \Sigma E_{\text{final}}$$

Graphical analysis is most often used during experimentation to determine mathematical relationships.

Example

What is the significance of the slope of the graph below?

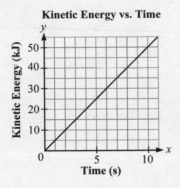

Kinetic Energy vs. Time

The graph shows kinetic energy with respect to time. The slope, *m*, of the graph is given by

$$m = \frac{y_2 - y_1}{x_2 - x_1}$$

$$= \frac{E_{k2} - E_{k1}}{t_2 - t_1}$$

$$m = \frac{\Delta E}{\Delta t}$$

If you compare this equation with those on the data sheet, you will see that it closely resembles

the equation for power, $P = \dfrac{\Delta E}{t}$.

Therefore, the slope of the energy vs. time graph is the power of the system described.

Example

A puck glides down an inclined air table. If it starts from rest, and the table is inclined at 12.0°, what speed will the puck have after moving 35.0 cm?

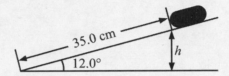

The total energy doesn't change so:
$$\sum E_i = \sum E_f$$
$$E_p + E_k = E_p' + E_k'$$
$$mgh + 0 = 0 + \frac{1}{2}mv^2$$
$$v = \sqrt{2gh}$$
$$= \sqrt{2(9.81 \text{ m/s}^2)(0.35 \text{ m})\sin 12.0°}$$
$$= 1.19 \text{ m/s}$$

Note: The lowest point of the path was taken to be zero potential energy. You can choose the zero potential energy to be anywhere you want.

Note: Also, the path taken does not matter. Only the vertical displacement from the start to the finish matters.

Example

A bead slides on a wire, as shown here. Ignoring friction, what will be the speed of the bead at point B?

$v = 2.40 \text{ m/s}$

B

1.20 m

0.80 m

Assume ground level as zero potential energy.

$$\Sigma E_i = \Sigma E_f$$
$$E_p + E_k = E_p' + E_k'$$
$$mgh + \frac{1}{2}mv^2 = mgh' + \frac{1}{2}mv'^2$$
$$gh + \frac{1}{2}v^2 = gh' + \frac{1}{2}v'^2$$
$$gh - gh' + \frac{1}{2}v^2 = \frac{1}{2}v'^2$$
$$2g(h - h') + v^2 = v'^2$$

Inserting known values:
$$v'^2 = 2(9.81\ \text{m/s}^2)(1.20\ \text{m} - 0.80\ \text{m}) + (2.40\ \text{m/s})^2$$
$$v'^2 = 13.61\ \text{m}^2/\text{s}^2$$
$$v' = 3.69\ \text{m/s}$$

Note: This question could have been done by taking zero potential energy at point B. In this case, this would have made $h = 0.40$ m and $h' = 0$.

Practice Questions: NR6, 18, 19

C2.4   recall work as a measure of the mechanical energy transferred and power as the rate of doing work

C2.5   describe power qualitatively and quantitatively

C2.6   describe, qualitatively, the change in mechanical energy in a system that is not isolated

RELATIONSHIP BETWEEN WORK AND POWER

Work is a force applied through a distance against a resistance. Power is the rate of doing work.
$$W = Fd$$
$$P = \frac{W}{t}$$
$$= \frac{Fd}{t}$$

In accordance with Newton's three laws of motion, you need to consider friction, force, and work when you calculate the conservation of mechanical energy.

This is because the system will respond by changing its total energy when work is done on a system. This is expressed algebraically as:
$$W = \Delta E$$

This can be rewritten in many different forms. For example, $W = \Delta E = E_f - E_i$

Work is also a scalar quantity but if the system gains energy, the work done is positive, and if the system loses energy, the work done is negative.

Example

A 1 500 kg car moving at 20.0 m/s over level ground slows to 10.0 m/s while travelling 400 m. Find the work done and the force of friction.

First, since the road surface is level, the potential energy does not change. Thus, $E_p = 0$ in this case. That way, you have no potential energy to track.
$$W = \Delta E = E_f - E_i$$
$$= E_{k(\text{final})} - E_{k(\text{initial})}$$
$$= \frac{1}{2}mv_f^2 - \frac{1}{2}mv_i^2$$
$$= \frac{1}{2}(1\ 500\ \text{kg})(10.0\ \text{m/s})^2$$
$$- \frac{1}{2}(1\ 500\ \text{kg})(20.0\ \text{m/s})^2$$
$$= -2.25 \times 10^5\ \text{J}$$

The negative value indicates a loss of energy in the system. This is typical with friction.

Use the work to find the force of friction.
$$W = Fd \Rightarrow F_f = \frac{W}{d}$$
$$= \frac{-2.25 \times 10^5\ \text{J}}{400\ \text{m}}$$
$$= -562.5\ \text{N}$$
$$= -563\ \text{N}$$

Note: The negative sign on the friction force means that it is in the opposite direction from the motion of the car.

When the direction of the force is not in the direction of displacement, the work done can be found using:
$$W = Fd\cos\theta$$

Where θ is the angle between F and d.

Example

A 20.0 kg box slides 2.00 m down a ramp that is inclined at 30.0°. If there is a 40.0 N force of friction acting on it, then what will the speed of the box be at the bottom of the ramp?

The change in the height of the box is $2.00 \text{ m} \times \sin 30.0° = 1.00 \text{ m}$.

Work done on the box

$$W = \Delta E$$
$$= E_f - E_i$$
$$F_f d = E_{k(\text{bottom})} - E_{p(\text{top})}$$
$$F_f d = \frac{1}{2}mv_f^2 - mgh$$
$$\frac{1}{2}mv_f^2 = F_f d + mgh$$
$$v_f^2 = \frac{2(F_f d + mgh)}{m}$$
$$v_f = \sqrt{\frac{2(F_f d + mgh)}{m}}$$
$$= \sqrt{\frac{2\left(\begin{array}{c}(-40.0 \text{ N})(2.00 \text{ m}) \\ +(20.0 \text{ kg})(9.81 \text{ m/s}^2)(1.00 \text{ m})\end{array}\right)}{20.0 \text{ kg}}}$$
$$= 3.41 \text{ m/s}$$

This question can also be broken down into small steps.

Work done (system loses this energy).
$$W = F_f d$$
$$= (-40.0 \text{ N})(2.00 \text{ m})$$
$$= -80.0 \text{ J}$$

Initial energy (all potential).
$$E_p = mgh$$
$$= (20.0 \text{ kg})(9.81 \text{ m/s}^2)(1.00 \text{ m})$$
$$= 196.2 \text{ J}$$

Final energy (all kinetic).
$$E_k = 196.2 \text{ J} - 80.0 \text{ J}$$
$$= 116.2 \text{ J}$$
$$= \frac{1}{2}mv^2$$
$$\Rightarrow v = \sqrt{\frac{2E_k}{m}}$$
$$= \sqrt{\frac{2 \times 116.2 \text{ J}}{20.0 \text{ kg}}}$$
$$= 3.41 \text{ m/s}$$

Practice Questions: NR4, 13, 14, 16, NR7

PRACTICE QUESTIONS—CIRCULAR MOTION, WORK, AND ENERGY

Use the following information to answer the next question.

The moon orbits Earth with an average period of 27.3 days at a radius of 3.84×10^5 km. (The radius of the orbit includes the radii of Earth and the moon.)

CHALLENGER QUESTION

1. The centripetal acceleration of the moon in its orbit around Earth is
   A. 2.72×10^{-6} m/s^2
   B. 2.72×10^{-3} m/s^2
   C. 2.72×10^2 m/s^2
   D. 2.72×10^6 m/s^2

2. A ball tied to the end of a string moves in a circular path. If the frequency of the motion is doubled while the length of the string stays constant, how will the acceleration of the ball change?
   A. Reduced by a factor of 4
   B. Reduced by a factor of 2
   C. Increased by a factor of 4
   D. Increased by a factor of 2

CHALLENGER QUESTION

3. An old phonograph record of the "Mothers of Invention" turns at 33.3 rpm (revolutions per minute) on a turntable. A 1.0×10^{-5} kg lint ball sits 5.0 cm from the central hole. If the ball does **not** move, relative to the record, the frictional force on the ball is
   A. 0 N
   B. 2.2×10^{-2} N
   C. 9.8×10^{-5} N
   D. 6.1×10^{-6} N

Use the following information to answer the next three questions.

A particular ride at a carnival, called "The Rotor," is a cylinder that revolves at high speeds. The riders stand with their backs against the inside wall of the cylinder. When the cylinder reaches a frequency of 0.50 Hz, the floor drops away from the riders' feet and they are stuck to the wall.

4. If the cylinder has a radius of 5.00 m, what is the value of the acceleration?
   A. 0.49 m/s^2
   B. 49 m/s^2
   C. 59 m/s^2
   D. 5.9×10^2 m/s^2

Numerical Response

1. Using your answer from the previous multiple choice question, the centripetal force a 75 kg person would experience on the ride can be expressed in scientific notation as $a.b \times 10^w$ N. The value of ab is ___. (Record your answer as a **two-digit** number.)

5. The minimum coefficient of friction needed so that the 75 kg person will stick to the walls when the floor drops is

A. 0.020   B. 0.20

C. 0.50   D. 5.0

Use the following information to answer the next two questions

A 300 g ball is swinging in a vertical circle on the end of a 1.20 m string. The speed of the ball at the bottom of the swing is 8.50 m/s.

6. The tension in the string is

A. 2.94 N

B. 15.1 N

C. 18.1 N

D. 21.0 N

7. The minimum speed needed at the top of the circle is

A. 3.43 m/s

B. 7.78 m/s

C. 11.8 m/s

D. 9.16 m/s

Use the following information to answer the next question.

The International Space Station (ISS) orbits Earth at an average altitude of 390 km and completes one orbit every 92 min.

8. What type of force is acting on the ISS to keep it moving at a constant altitude?

A. frictional

B. electrostatic

C. gravitational

D. electromagnetic

9. The largest moon in the solar system is Ganymede, which orbits around the planet Jupiter. Given that the radius of its orbit around Jupiter is 1.07×10^6 km, and it completes one orbit every 7.16 days, what is the mass of Jupiter?

A. 1.02×10^{15} kg

B. 1.17×10^{33} kg

C. 1.89×10^{27} kg

D. 3.53×10^{36} kg

10. The centre of Earth is a distance of 1.50×10^{11} m away from the centre of the sun and it takes 365 days for Earth to orbit the sun once. Therefore, the mass of the sun is

A. 2.01×10^{30} kg

B. 4.04×10^{30} kg

C. 4.04×10^{22} kg

D. 6.03×10^{22} kg

Numerical Response

2. Planet La Roche is 1.74×10^{11} m away from its sun, and it takes 233 days to orbit the sun. Another planet, L'eau, orbits the same sun in 310 days. If L'eau is $a.bc \times 10^d$ km from its sun, then the correct value for *abcd* is _____.

Use the following information to answer the next two questions.

A vehicle uses the Global Positioning System's (GPS) satellite navigation system, which tells drivers their exact position and the best route to their destination. There is a network of global positioning satellites that orbit Earth at an altitude of 2.01×10^7 m.

11. The orbital period of these satellites is
    A. 7.88 h
    B. 11.9 h
    C. 24.0 h
    D. 713 h

Use your recorded answer from the previous question to answer the next question.

Numerical Response

3. Using your answer from the previous question, the speed of these satellites is _____ km/s. (Record your answer to **three** significant digits.)

Use the following information to answer the next question.

In the construction of large buildings, powerful cranes are used to lift concrete and steel compounds, at a constant speed, to the top of the building being constructed.

12. Ignoring the initial acceleration of the object lifted, which one of the following statements about the lifting done by the crane is **incorrect?**
    A. Work is done during the lift.
    B. Mechanical energy is transferred.
    C. Potential energy changes occur to the object being lifted.
    D. Kinetic energy changes occur to the object being lifted.

13. A force of 40.0 N is applied to a rope that makes an angle of 60.0° to the horizontal. An object attached to the rope moves horizontally along a frictionless surface a distance of 5.00 m. How much work is done?
    A. 50.0 J
    B. 100 J
    C. 200 J
    D. 400 J

Numerical Response

4. An express elevator has an average speed of 9.1 m/s as it rises from the ground floor to the 100th floor, which is 402 m above the ground. Assuming the elevator has a total mass of 1.1×10^3 kg, the power supplied by the lifting motor is $ab \times 10^c$ W (in scientific notation). The value of *abc* is _____. (Record your answer as a **three-digit** number.)

Use the following information to answer the next question.

Scientists at the University of Alberta are part of a research team that uses the TRIUMF cyclotron to accelerate and collide protons. Protons are accelerated in the cyclotron to a speed of 225 000 km/s in $\dfrac{1}{3\ 000}$ of a second and then the protons are directed at a solid target. Upon striking the target, the protons are "broken" into other particles that are then studied.

14. What is the amount of work required to accelerate a proton with mass of 1.67×10^{-27} kg from rest to 225 000 km/s? (Ignore special relativity—assume that the mass of the proton is constant.)

   A. 1.88×10^{-19} J

   B. 4.23×10^{-17} J

   C. 4.23×10^{-11} J

   D. 8.45×10^{-11} J

Numerical Response

5. A 2 000 g artillery shell is shot vertically upward. It has 3.60×10^3 J of kinetic energy as it leaves the gun on the ground. Ignoring air resistance, the height to which the shell will rise is _____ m. (Record your answer to **three** significant digits.)

15. A rock resting at the edge of a cliff is dropped over the edge. Ignoring friction, which of the following statements is **false**?

   A. The potential energy increases as the kinetic energy decreases.

   B. The mechanical energy of the rock at the top equals the mechanical energy at the bottom.

   C. The potential energy decreases at the same rate as the kinetic energy increases.

   D. The potential energy of the rock (relative to the ground) at the top is greater than the kinetic energy at the top.

Numerical Response

6. A compressed spring has a potential energy of 10 J. The maximum energy it can impart to a 1.2 kg ball is ___ J. (Record your answer to **two** significant digits.)

16. Two carts, each with a spring bumper, collide head-on. At one point during the collision, both carts are at rest for an instant. At that instant, the kinetic energy that the carts originally possessed is almost completely

   A. lost to friction

   B. transformed into heat and sound

   C. converted into kinetic energy in the spring bumpers

   D. converted into potential energy in the spring bumpers

17. A truck with a mass of 4.00×10^4 kg is travelling at 27.78 m/s. If the driver reduces the truck's speed to 16.67 m/s, then the truck's kinetic energy has changed by

A. -2.22×10^4 J

B. -9.88×10^6 J

C. -3.20×10^7 J

D. -1.28×10^8 J

Numerical Response

7. A pump delivers 56.0 L/min of water from a well that is 20.0 m deep. A 1.00 L volume of water has a mass of 1.00 kg. The work done by the pump in 1.00 s is _____ J. (Record your answer to **three** significant digits.)

Use the following information to answer the next question.

After performing a trick above the rim of a skateboard ramp, a 56 kg skateboarder lands on the ramp 3.5 m above ground level with a downward velocity of 4.0 m/s.

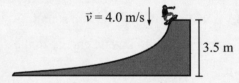

$\vec{v} = 4.0$ m/s ↓

3.5 m

Friction in the wheels of the skateboard and air resistance causes a loss of 9.0×10^2 J of mechanical energy.

18. The skateboarder's speed at the bottom of the ramp will be

A. 6.0 m/s

B. 7.2 m/s

C. 9.2 m/s

D. 11 m/s

Use the following information to answer the next question.

During an archery competition, an arrow of mass 35.0 g is fired horizontally with a speed of 1.10×10^2 m/s at a target fixed to a wall. The arrow does not drop significantly during its flight. The arrow penetrates the target to a depth of 5.00 cm and is brought to a complete stop.

19. The kinetic energy of the arrow as it leaves the bow is

A. 4.24×10^5 J

B. 2.12×10^5 J

C. 4.24×10^2 J

D. 2.12×10^2 J

ANSWERS AND SOLUTIONS—PRACTICE QUESTIONS

1. B	6. D	11. B	NR5. 183	18. B
2. C	7. A	NR3. 3.89	15. A	19. D
3. D	8. C	12. D	NR6. 10	
4. B	9. C	13. B	16. D	
NR1. 37	10. A	NR4. 984	17. B	
5. B	NR2. 2108	14. C	NR7. 183	

1. B

$$a_c = \frac{v^2}{r} \text{ and } v = \frac{2\pi r}{T}$$

Substitute to get the magnitude of the centripetal acceleration.

$$a_c = \frac{\left(\frac{2\pi r}{T}\right)^2}{r}$$
$$= \frac{4\pi^2 r}{T^2}$$

$$a_c = \frac{4\pi^2 \left(3.84 \times 10^8 \text{ m}\right)}{\left(27.3 \text{ d} \times 24 \text{ h/d} \times 3\,600 \text{ s/h}\right)^2}$$
$$= 2.72 \times 10^{-3} \text{ m/s}^2$$

2. C

$$a_c = \frac{v^2}{r} \text{ and } v = \frac{2\pi r}{T}$$

Substitute the value of speed

$$a_c = \frac{\left(\frac{2\pi r}{T}\right)^2}{r} \text{ and } f = \frac{1}{T}$$

Magnitude of acceleration
$$a_c = \frac{4\pi^2 f^2 r^2}{r}$$
$$= 4\pi^2 r f^2$$

As $a \propto f^2$, if f doubles, a_c increases by a factor of 4.

3. D

$\vec{F}_c = \vec{F}_f$ since the lint does not move in relation to the record.

$$F_c = \frac{mv^2}{r}$$
$$= \frac{4\pi^2 mr}{T^2}$$

$$T = \frac{1 \text{ rev}}{(33.3 \text{ rev/min})} \times \frac{60 \text{ s}}{1 \text{ min}}$$
$$= 1.80 \text{ s}$$

$$\therefore F_c = \frac{4\pi^2 \left(1.0 \times 10^{-5} \text{ kg}\right)(0.050 \text{ m})}{(1.80 \text{ s})^2}$$
$$= 6.1 \times 10^{-6} \text{ N}$$

4. B

Value of the centripetal acceleration is $a_c = \frac{v^2}{r}$

and speed is $v = \frac{2\pi r}{T}$.

Substituting for v

$$a_c = \frac{\left(\frac{2\pi r}{T}\right)^2}{r}$$
$$= \frac{4\pi^2 r}{T^2}$$

again $T = \frac{1}{f}$

$$= \frac{1}{0.50 \text{ Hz}}$$
$$= 2.00 \text{ s}$$

Substituting for T,

$$a_c = \frac{4\pi^2(5.00 \text{ m})}{(2.00 \text{ s})^2}$$
$$= 49.3 \text{ m/s}^2$$

NR 1   37

$$F_c = ma_c$$
$$= (75 \text{ kg})(49.3 \text{ m/s}^2)$$
$$= 3\ 697.5 \text{ N}$$
$$= 3.7 \times 10^3 \text{ N}$$

5.   B

The normal force from the wall is the net centripetal force here, so your answer to question NR1 is the normal force.

The force of friction must equal the force of gravity so a person does not slide down the wall.

$$F_N = ma_c$$
$$= (75 \text{ kg})(49.3 \text{ m/s}^2)$$
$$= 3.70 \times 10^3 \text{ N}$$
$$F_f = mg$$
$$= (75 \text{ kg})(9.81 \text{ m/s}^2)$$
$$= 736 \text{ N}$$
$$F_f = \mu F_N$$
$$\mu = \frac{F_f}{F_N}$$
$$= \frac{736 \text{ N}}{3.70 \times 10^3 \text{ N}}$$
$$= 0.20$$

6.   D

At the bottom of the swing, the tension in the string is upward, and the force of gravity is downward. Net force on the ball is given by

$$\vec{F}_{net} = \vec{F}_c$$
$$= \vec{F}_T + \vec{F}_g$$

The ball is accelerating toward the centre of the circle, so the tension is larger than gravity. The magnitude of the centripetal force is

$$F_c = F_T - F_g$$
$$F_T = \frac{mv^2}{r} + mg$$
$$= \frac{(0.300 \text{ kg})(8.50 \text{ m/s})^2}{1.20 \text{ m}}$$
$$\quad + (0.300 \text{ kg})(9.81 \text{ m/s}^2)$$
$$= 21.0 \text{ N}$$

7.   A

When the speed at the top is a minimum, the centripetal force is equal to the magnitude of the force due to gravity. So the tension in the string must be zero.

$$0 + F_g = F_c$$
$$= ma_c$$
$$mg = \frac{mv^2}{r}$$
$$v = \sqrt{gr}$$
$$= \sqrt{(9.81 \text{ m/s}^2)(1.20 \text{ m})}$$
$$= 3.43 \text{ m/s}$$

8.   C

Gravity supplies the centripetal force needed to keep the ISS in orbit. (Assuming no resistance from air or other matter, inertia would keep the station moving at a constant velocity.) However, since there is some resistance in space, occasionally rockets are used to maintain velocity.

9.   C

$$T = 7.16 \text{ d} \times \frac{24.0 \text{ h}}{1.00 \text{ d}} \times \frac{3\ 600 \text{ s}}{1.00 \text{ h}}$$
$$= 6.19 \times 10^5 \text{ s}$$
$$F_c = F_g \text{ so}$$
$$\frac{4\pi^2 r m_G}{T^2} = \frac{Gm_J m_G}{r^2}$$

Rearranging, the mass of Jupiter is

$$m_J = \frac{4\pi^2 r^3}{GT^2}$$

$$= \frac{4(3.14)^2(1.07 \times 10^9 \text{ m})^3}{\left(6.67 \times 10^{-11} \frac{\text{N} \cdot \text{m}^2}{\text{kg}^2}\right)(6.19 \times 10^5 \text{ s})^2}$$
$$= 1.89 \times 10^{27} \text{ kg}$$

10.   A

It takes Earth 365 days to orbit the sun.

$$T = 365 \text{ d} \times \frac{24.0 \text{ h}}{1.00 \text{ d}} \times \frac{3\ 600 \text{ s}}{1.00 \text{ h}}$$
$$= 3.15 \times 10^7 \text{ s}$$
$$a_c = \frac{4\pi^2 r}{T^2}$$
$$= \frac{4\pi^2(1.5 \times 10^{11} \text{ m})}{(3.15 \times 10^7 \text{ s})^2}$$
$$= 5.97 \times 10^{-3} \text{ m/s}^2$$

Equating the magnitude of gravitational and centripetal forces,

$$F_c = F_g$$

$$m_E a_c = \frac{G m_E m_S}{r^2}$$

so $m_S = \dfrac{a_c r^2}{G}$

$$m_S = \frac{\left(5.97 \times 10^{-3} \text{ m/s}^2\right)\left(1.50 \times 10^{11} \text{ m}\right)^2}{\left(6.67 \times 10^{-11} \dfrac{\text{N} \cdot \text{m}^2}{\text{kg}^2}\right)}$$

$$= 2.01 \times 10^{30} \text{ kg}$$

NR 2   2108

Using Kepler's third law, $\dfrac{R^3}{T^2} = $ constant;

then $\dfrac{R_{LR}^3}{T_{LR}^2} = \dfrac{R_{LE}^3}{T_{LE}^2}$

$$\frac{\left(1.74 \times 10^{11} \text{ m}\right)^3}{\left(233 \text{ d}\right)^2} = \frac{R_{LE}^3}{\left(310 \text{ d}\right)^2}$$

$$R_{LE}^3 = \frac{\left(1.74 \times 10^{11} \text{ m}\right)^3 \left(310 \text{ d}\right)^2}{\left(233 \text{ d}\right)^2}$$

$$R_{LE} = 2.10 \times 10^{11} \text{ m} \times \frac{1 \text{ km}}{1\,000 \text{ m}}$$

$$= 2.10 \times 10^8 \text{ km}$$

11. B

The distance from Earth's centre is

$$r = 6.37 \times 10^6 \text{ m} + 2.01 \times 10^7 \text{ m}$$

$$= 2.647 \times 10^7 \text{ m}$$

As the satellites maintain constant distance from the centre of Earth, $\vec{F}_c$ must equal $\vec{F}_g$.

$$F_c = F_g$$

$$\frac{4\pi^2 r m_s}{T^2} = G \frac{m_s m_E}{r^2}$$

The mass of the satellite appears on both sides of the equation, so m_s cancels out.

$$T = \sqrt{\frac{4\pi^2 r^3}{G m_E}}$$

$$= \sqrt{\frac{4\pi^2 \left(2.647 \times 10^7 \text{ m}\right)^3}{\left(6.67 \times 10^{-11} \dfrac{\text{N} \cdot \text{m}^2}{\text{kg}^2}\right)\left(5.98 \times 10^{24} \text{ kg}\right)}}$$

$$= 4.28 \times 10^4 \text{ s}$$

$$= \left(4.28 \times 10^4 \text{ s}\right)\left(\frac{1.00 \text{ h}}{3\,600 \text{ s}}\right) = 11.9 \text{ h}$$

Note: These satellites are not geosynchronous. Geosynchronous orbits occur where $T = 24$ h, such that the satellite is always above the same point on Earth.

NR 3   3.89

$$T = 11.9 \text{ h}$$

$$= 4.28 \times 10^4 \text{ s}$$

$$v = \frac{2\pi r}{T}$$

$$= \frac{2\pi \left(2.647 \times 10^7 \text{ m}\right)}{4.28 \times 10^4 \text{ s}}$$

$$= 3\,886 \text{ m/s}$$

$$= 3.89 \text{ km/s}$$

12. D

During the lift, because the object is lifted at a constant speed, the kinetic energy is constant. Therefore, kinetic energy does not change as the object is lifted.

13. B

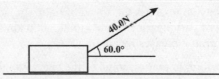

The x-component of the applied force is used to do work, assuming there is no friction.

$$W = F d \cos\theta$$

$$= \left(40.0 \text{ N}\right)\left(5.00 \text{ m}\right)\left(\cos 60.0°\right)$$

$$= 100 \text{ J}$$

NR 4   984

$$P = \frac{W}{t}$$

Neither work nor time is given, but both can be determined from the information given.

$$W = \Delta E_p$$
$$\Delta E_p = mgh$$
$$= (1.1 \times 10^3 \text{ kg})(9.81 \text{ m/s}^2)(402 \text{ m})$$
$$= 4.34 \times 10^6 \text{ J}$$
$$d = vt$$
$$\text{so } t = \frac{d}{v}$$
$$= \frac{402 \text{ m}}{9.1 \text{ m/s}}$$
$$= 44.2 \text{ s}$$

$$\text{Power} = \frac{4.34 \times 10^6 \text{ J}}{44.2 \text{ s}}$$
$$= 9.8 \times 10^4 \text{ W}$$

14. C

$$W = \Delta E_k$$

Since the particle starts from rest, the initial velocity is 0 and, therefore, the initial E_k is 0.

$$W = \frac{1}{2}mv_f^2$$

Remember to convert km/s to m/s.
225 000 km/s = 225 000 000 m/s

$$W = \frac{1}{2}(1.67 \times 10^{-27} \text{ kg})(2.25 \times 10^8 \text{ m/s})^2$$
$$= 4.23 \times 10^{-11} \text{ J}$$

Note: According to Einstein's theory of relativity, the mass of an object increases as the object's velocity approaches the speed of light. In fact, the mass of particles accelerated to 225 000 km/s in the cyclotron increases by about 50%.

Therefore, in reality, some of the energy applied to these particles increases their mass rather than increasing their speed.

NR 5   183

Assume all of the kinetic energy converts into potential energy.

$$E_p = mgh$$
$$h = \frac{E_p}{mg}$$
$$= \frac{3.60 \times 10^3 \text{ J}}{(2.00 \text{ kg})(9.81 \text{ m/s}^2)}$$
$$= 183 \text{ m}$$

15. A

The potential energy of the rock would decrease as the rock fell and its kinetic energy would increase. Therefore, **A** is false.

NR 6   10

Because energy is conserved, the maximum energy (any form) that the spring can impart to the 1.2 kg ball is 10 J.

16. D

The bumpers flex as the carts come together. Some of their kinetic energy is converted to sound and heat but most is stored as elastic potential energy in the bumpers. (The bumpers return much of the energy as kinetic energy after they spring back.)

17. B

Kinetic energy decreases as speed decreases.

$$\Delta E_k = \frac{1}{2}m(v_f^2 - v_i^2)$$
$$v_f = 16.67 \text{ m/s}$$
$$v_i = 27.78 \text{ m/s}$$
$$\Delta E_k = \frac{1}{2}(4.00 \times 10^4 \text{ kg})((16.67 \text{ m/s})^2 - (27.78 \text{ m/s})^2)$$
$$= -9.88 \times 10^6 \text{ J}$$

NR 7   183

A 1.00 L volume of water has a mass of 1.00 kg.

So $\dfrac{56.0 \text{ L/min}}{60 \text{ s/min}} = 0.933$ L/s

$= 0.933$ kg/s

In 1.00 s, the pump moves 0.933 kg of water.

It is necessary to find how much work this requires.

$W = Fd$

$= mgd$

$= (0.933 \text{ kg})(9.81 \text{ m/s}^2)(20.0 \text{ m})$

$= 183$ J

18. B

The skateboarder's kinetic energy at the bottom of the ramp will be equal to his (or her) total mechanical energy at the top of the ramp minus the energy lost due to work done by friction, which escapes as heat.

$E_{p \text{ top}} = mgh$

$= (56 \text{ kg})(9.81 \text{ m/s}^2)(3.5 \text{ m})$

$= 1.92 \times 10^3$ J

$E_{k \text{ top}} = \dfrac{1}{2}mv^2$

$= \dfrac{1}{2}(56 \text{ kg})(4.0 \text{ m/s})^2$

$= 4.48 \times 10^2$ J

$E_{\text{total top}} = 1.92 \times 10^3 \text{ J} + 4.48 \times 10^2 \text{ J}$

$= 2.37 \times 10^3$ J

$E_{k \text{ bottom}} = 2.37 \times 10^3 \text{ J} - 9.0 \times 10^2 \text{ J}$

$= 1.47 \times 10^3$ J

$E_k = \dfrac{1}{2}mv^2$

$\Rightarrow v = \sqrt{\dfrac{2E_k}{m}}$

$= \sqrt{\dfrac{2(1.47 \times 10^3 \text{ J})}{56 \text{ kg}}}$

$= 7.2$ m/s

19. D

The kinetic energy can be calculated using the following method:

$E_k = \dfrac{1}{2}mv^2$

$= \dfrac{1}{2}(0.035 \text{ kg})(1.10 \times 10^2 \text{ m/s})^2$

$= 2.12 \times 10^2$ J

UNIT TEST—CIRCULAR MOTION, WORK, AND ENERGY

1. The net force that causes the centripetal acceleration of the moon is
   A. the moon's inertia
   B. the gravity of the moon
   C. centripetal motion of the moon
   D. the gravitational attraction of Earth

Use the following information to answer the next question.

The TRIUMF cyclotron, located in Vancouver, British Columbia, accelerates protons at high speeds. When a beam of protons strikes a solid target, the protons are "broken" into other particles that can then be studied.

2. If a proton with a mass of 1.67×10^{-27} m/s and speed of 2.25×10^7 m/s travels in a circular path of diameter 18.0 m, what is the magnitude of the centripetal force acting on the proton?
   A. 1.68×10^{-28} N
   B. 4.18×10^{-26} N
   C. 4.69×10^{-14} N
   D. 9.39×10^{-14} N

Use the following information to answer the next question

Physicists at the University of Alberta are involved in an international experiment called OPAL3. They are studying electron-positron collisions using the Large Electron-Positron Collider (LEP) at the European Centre for Particle Physics (CERN) in Switzerland.
The LEP has a circumference of 27 km and can accelerate beams of electrons and positrons to almost the speed of light. Electrons orbit the collider in one direction and the oppositely charged positrons orbit in the opposite direction.

3. The time that it takes for an electron travelling at a speed of 2.99×10^8 m/s to complete one orbit of the LEP collider is
   A. 1.1×10^{-4} s
   B. 3.8×10^{-5} s
   C. 9.0×10^{-5} s
   D. 9.0×10^{-8} s

Use the following information to answer the next question.

A particular ride at a carnival, called "The Rotor," is a cylinder that revolves at high speeds. The riders stand with their backs against the inside wall of the cylinder. When the cylinder reaches a frequency of 0.50 Hz, the floor drops away from the riders' feet and they are stuck to the wall.

4. The type of acceleration described above is
   A. linear
   B. uniform
   C. centripetal
   D. gravitational

CHALLENGER QUESTION

5. A pilot in an air show does a vertical loop with a radius of 1 200 m. The plane is upside down at the top of the loop. If his mass is 90.0 kg and his apparent weight at the top of the loop is 1 850 N, at what speed is the airplane flying?
   A. 108 m/s
   B. 114 m/s
   C. 157 m/s
   D. 191 m/s

CHALLENGER QUESTION

Numerical Response

1. The solar system lies within the Milky Way galaxy. The sun is located about 3.0×10^{20} m from the centre of the galaxy. The sun orbits the centre of the galaxy once every 250 million years. Using this information, the approximate value of the galaxy's mass, expressed in scientific notation, is $b \times 10^w$ kg. The value for w is _____. (Record your answer as a **two-digit** number.)

Use the following information to answer the next question.

The motion of most objects in the universe are basically elliptical (elliptical includes circular), since these objects are in orbit around other objects. Moons orbit planets, planets orbit suns, solar systems orbit within galaxies.

6. Which of the following scientific laws docs **not** address the fact that systems of objects exist and the components of these systems move in elliptical orbits?

A. Kepler's first law

B. Kepler's second law

C. Newton's law of gravitation

D. Newton's third law of motion

Numerical Response

2. A truck, with a mass of 2.00×10^3 kg, is driving along a straight level road at 25.0 m/s when it runs out of gas. It slows down without braking and comes to rest in 300 m. The work done by frictional forces expressed in scientific notation is $-b \times 10^w$ J. The value of b is _____. (Record your answer as a **three-digit** number.)

Use the following information to answer the next question.

The first windmills, developed by the Persians in about the 5th century AD, were used to pump water for irrigation. Modern windmills are used to generate electricity by using the rotation of the blades to turn a generator.

7. If a windmill turns with a period of 1.0 s and generates 6.0 MW of electricity by moving a blade 91 m in one rotation, then the force on the blades is

A. 1.6×10^6 N

B. 5.7×10^9 N

C. 5.7×10^{12} N

D. 6.6×10^4 N

8. At a particular instant, a falling body has a potential energy nine times its kinetic energy. If the body continued to fall until its velocity were doubled, the ratio of its kinetic energy to its potential energy at this instant would be

A. 2:3

B. 2:5

C. 3:4

D. 5:7

Use the following information to answer the next question.

Solar panels are often used as power sources in remote areas. For example, they are used to power cathodic protection devices that prevent corrosion in oil pipe lines. They are also used to power pumps and motors.

Numerical Response

3. If a 1.00 m^2 solar panel, producing 102 W/m^2, is used to pump water to a height of 1.00 m, the mass of water (kg) that can be pumped up to the 1.00 m height in 1.00 s, assuming that the pump operates at 50.0% efficiency, is _____ kg. (Record your answer to **three** significant digits.)

9. In an inelastic collision, the energy that appears to be missing is converted into

   A. heat and force

   B. sound and heat

   C. sound and force

   D. speed and temperature

Use the following information to answer the next two questions.

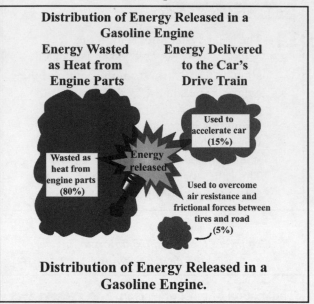

Distribution of Energy Released in a Gasoline Engine.

10. The maximum amount of energy that would be delivered to the drive train when 65.0 L of gasoline is burned is

   A. 1.51×10^2 MJ

   B. 1.96×10^3 MJ

   C. 3.93×10^2 MJ

   D. 9.82×10^3 MJ

Source: June 2001

11. The change in the kinetic energy of the car during the test drive is

   A. 9.60×10^3 J

   B. 1.15×10^5 J

   C. 1.73×10^5 J

   D. 1.80×10^5 J

Use the following information to answer the next three questions.

90 m Ski Jump

An elevation profile of the 90-m ski jump at Canada Olympic Park in Calgary is shown below. The skiers slide down a 111-m long ramp before taking off at the "table point." The distance from the table point to the "norm point" (the beginning of the steepest section of the landing hill) is 90 m, hence the name of the jump. Farther downhill, at the end of a straight section of 24.0 m, is the "critical point." If skiers fly past the critical point, it becomes dangerous to land because the landing hill starts to flatten out.

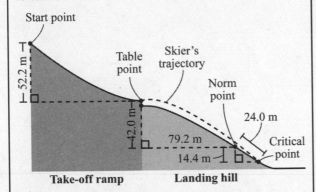

During a ski jumping competition, a skier's speed at the table point was 95 km/h, and she landed at the critical point with a speed of 85 km/h. The combined mass of the skier and her equipment was 60 kg.

12. The change in the skier's gravitational potential energy as she moved from the table point to the critical point was

   A. -2.5×10^4 J

   B. -3.3×10^4 J

   C. -3.6×10^4 J

   D. -6.7×10^4 J

13. Current ski jumping techniques actually slow down the ski jumpers on the way to the bottom of the hill. The skier's speed upon landing at the critical point was 85 km/h. What was the change in this skier's kinetic energy on her flight from the table point to the critical point?

   A. -8.4×10^1 J

   B. -3.0×10^2 J

   C. -4.2×10^3 J

   D. -5.4×10^4 J

14. The reduction in flight speed as a skier moves through the air is mainly due to the aerodynamic lift generated on the skier in "sailing position." The work done by this force acts to reduce the

   A. kinetic energy of the skier

   B. potential energy of the skier

   C. time spent in the air by the skier

   D. horizontal distance travelled by the skier

Use the following information to answer the next question.

The gravitational potential energy, kinetic energy, and mechanical energy of a bungee jumper during the free-fall portion of a jump are graphed below.

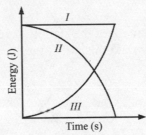

15. Lines *I*, *II*, and *III* represent, respectively,

   A. mechanical energy, gravitational potential energy, and kinetic energy

   B. mechanical energy, kinetic energy, and gravitational potential energy

   C. gravitational potential energy, mechanical energy, and kinetic energy

   D. kinetic energy, gravitational potential energy, and mechanical energy

Source: January 2002

Written Response

Use the following information to answer the next question.

The International Space Station (ISS) orbits Earth at an altitude of 390 km and completes one orbit every 92 min.

1. **a)** Calculate the speed of the space station in its orbit.

b) If the mass of the station were doubled, how would this affect the speed?

c) If the ISS were to orbit a planet with double Earth's mass at the same radius, how would this affect the speed of the station?

ANSWERS AND SOLUTIONS—UNIT TEST

1. D	5. D	7. D	10. C	14. A
2. D	NR1. 41	8. A	11. C	15. A
3 C	6. D	NR3. 5.20	12. B	WR1. See Solution
4. C	NR2. 6.25	9. B	13. C	

1. D

The net centripetal force on the moon points toward the centre of its orbit, and it is caused by the gravitational force exerted by Earth.

2. D

$$d = 2r$$
$$\Rightarrow r = \frac{1}{2}d$$
$$= \frac{18.0 \text{ m}}{2}$$
$$= 9.00 \text{ m}$$
$$F_c = \frac{mv^2}{r}$$
$$= \frac{\left(1.67 \times 10^{-27} \text{ kg}\right)\left(2.25 \times 10^7 \text{ m/s}\right)^2}{9.00 \text{ m}}$$
$$F_c = 9.39 \times 10^{-14} \text{ N}$$

3. C

$$T = \frac{d}{v}$$
$$= \frac{2.7 \times 10^4 \text{ m}}{2.99 \times 10^8 \text{ m/s}}$$
$$= 9.0 \times 10^{-5} \text{ s}$$

4. C

The type of acceleration is centripetal acceleration. This effect relies on the inertia of the people, which keeps them pressed against the walls. This is what causes the people within this frame to experience the centrifugal pseudo-force.

5. D

The pilot experiences two forces—gravity and the normal force from his seat.

His apparent weight is the normal force. Both forces are downward, as is his acceleration.

$$F_{net} = ma_c$$
$$= \frac{mv^2}{r}$$
$$F_{net} = F_N + mg$$
$$\frac{mv^2}{r} = F_N + mg$$
$$v^2 = \frac{r\left(F_N + mg\right)}{m}$$
$$v = \sqrt{\frac{r\left(F_N + mg\right)}{m}}$$
$$= \sqrt{\frac{1\,200 \text{ m}\left(1\,850 \text{ N} + \left(90.0 \text{ kg}\right)\left(9.81 \text{ m/s}^2\right)\right)}{90.0 \text{ kg}}}$$
$$= 191 \text{ m/s}$$

NR 1   41

$$T = 250 \times 10^6 \text{ y} \times \frac{365.25 \text{ d}}{\text{y}} \times \frac{24.0 \text{ h}}{\text{d}} \times \frac{3\,600 \text{ s}}{\text{h}}$$
$$= 7.89 \times 10^{15} \text{ s}$$

Again $F_c = F_g$

$$\frac{4\pi^2 m_2 r}{T^2} = \frac{Gm_1 m_2}{r^2}$$
$$m_1 = \frac{4\pi^2 r^3}{GT^2}$$
$$m_1 = \frac{4\pi^2 \left(3.0 \times 10^{20} \text{ m}\right)^3}{\left(6.67 \times 10^{-11} \frac{\text{N} \cdot \text{m}^2}{\text{kg}^2}\right)\left(7.89 \times 10^{15} \text{ s}\right)^2}$$
$$= 2.6 \times 10^{41} \text{ kg}$$

Therefore, $w = 41$.

6. D

Since Kepler's laws describe planetary orbits and Newton's laws describe gravity, both are useful. Newton's third law of motion "every action has an equal and opposite reaction" is not very useful for describing orbits or gravity.

NR 2   6.25

$$W_f = \Delta E$$
$$= E_f - E_i$$
$$= 0 - \frac{1}{2}mv^2$$
$$= -\frac{1}{2}(2\ 000\ \text{kg})(25.0\ \text{m/s})^2$$
$$= -6.25 \times 10^5\ \text{J}$$

7. D

For one turn:
6.0 MW = 6.0 MJ/s

$$W = Pt$$
$$= 6.0 \times 10^6\ \text{J/s} \times 1.0\ \text{s}$$
$$= 6.0 \times 10^6\ \text{J}$$

$$W = Fd$$
$$F = \frac{W}{d}$$
$$= \frac{6.0 \times 10^6\ \text{J}}{91\ \text{m}}$$
$$= 6.6 \times 10^4\ \text{N}$$

8. A

Let E_k be the initial instantaneous kinetic energy that the body possesses. Then the initial potential energy that the body has is given as $9E_k$.

This means that the total mechanical energy of the system at that instant is given by

$$E_m = E_p + E_k$$
$$= 9E_k + E_k$$
$$= 10E_k$$

Since kinetic energy is given by the equation $E_k = \frac{1}{2}mv^2$, and the mass is constant, when the velocity is doubled its kinetic energy is quadrupled since

$$E'_k = \frac{1}{2}m(v')^2$$
$$= \frac{1}{2}m(2v)^2$$
$$= 4\left(\frac{1}{2}mv^2\right)$$
$$= 4E_k$$

Since mechanical energy is conserved, the potential energy that the body possesses when it's kinetic energy has quadrupled will be

$$E'_p = E_m - E'_k$$
$$= 10E_k - 4E_k$$
$$= 6E_k$$

Hence the ratio of its kinetic energy to its potential energy at this second position will be

$$\frac{E'_k}{E'_p} = \frac{4E_k}{6E_k}$$
$$= \frac{2}{3}$$
$$= 2 : 3$$

NR 3   5.20

$$P = 102 \text{ W/m}^2 \times 1.00 \text{ m}^2$$
$$= 102 \text{ W}$$
$$\Delta E = Pt$$
$$= (102 \text{ W})(1.00 \text{ s})$$
$$= 102 \text{ J}$$
$$E_p = mgh$$

Since the pump operates at 50% efficiency

$$\left(\frac{50.0}{100}\right)(102 \text{ J}) = m(9.81 \text{ N/kg})(1.00 \text{ m})$$
$$m = 5.20 \text{ kg}$$

9. B

Energy can transform into other forms of energy. Sound and heat are two forms of energy. Force, temperature, and speed are not forms of energy.

10. C

80% of the energy is wasted. The remaining 20% is used to overcome friction, air resistance, and to accelerate the car. The energy delivered to the drive train of the car is therefore 20% multiplied by the volume of fuel, multiplied by the rate of energy per unit volume.

$$E = 0.200 \times 65.0 \text{ L} \times \frac{30.2 \text{ MJ}}{\text{L}}$$
$$= 3.93 \times 10^2 \text{ MJ}$$

11. C

$$\Delta E = E_{k_{final}} - E_{k_{initial}}$$
$$= \frac{1}{2}mv_f^2 - \frac{1}{2}mv_i^2$$
$$= \frac{1}{2}(1.60 \times 10^3 \text{ kg})(15.0 \text{ m/s})^2$$
$$\quad - \frac{1}{2}(1.60 \times 10^3 \text{ kg})(3.00 \text{ m/s})^2$$
$$= 1.73 \times 10^5 \text{ J}$$

12. B

$$E_p = mgh$$
$$\Delta E_p = E_{p_{final}} - E_{p_{initial}}$$
$$= 0 - (60 \text{ kg})(9.81 \text{ m/s}^2)(42.0 \text{ m} + 14.4 \text{ m})$$
$$= -3.3 \times 10^4 \text{ J}$$

13. C

$$E_k = \frac{1}{2}mv^2$$
$$\Delta E_k = E_{k_{final}} - E_{k_{initial}}$$
$$= \frac{1}{2}(60 \text{ kg})\left(\frac{85\ 000 \text{ m}}{3600 \text{ s}}\right)^2$$
$$\quad - \frac{1}{2}(60 \text{ kg})\left(\frac{95\ 000 \text{ m}}{3600 \text{ s}}\right)^2$$
$$= -4.2 \times 10^3 \text{ J}$$

14. A

Reduction in flight speed results in a reduction in her kinetic energy because $E_k = \frac{1}{2}mv^2$. So kinetic energy is directly proportional to the square of the speed. If the speed is reduced then the kinetic energy will also be reduced.

15. A

Mechanical energy, which is the sum of kinetic and gravitational potential energies, does not change in a conservative system. Gravitational potential energy decreases as height decreases, while kinetic energy increases as speed increases.

1. **a)** *Calculate the speed of the space station in its orbit.*

$$v = \frac{2\pi r}{T}$$
$$= \frac{2\pi \left(3.90 \times 10^5 \text{ m} + 6.37 \times 10^6 \text{ m}\right)}{(92 \text{ min})(60 \text{ s/min})}$$
$$= 7.7 \times 10^3 \text{ m/s}$$

b) *If the mass of the station were doubled, how would this affect the speed?*

$$F_c = F_g$$
$$\frac{\cancel{m}_s v^2}{r} = \frac{Gm_E \cancel{m}_s}{r^2}$$

As m_s is not a factor, m_s does not affect v.

Therefore, if the mass of the station were doubled, its speed would not be affected.

c) *If the ISS were to orbit a planet with double Earth's mass at the same radius, how would this affect the speed of the station?*

Let v = the speed of the ISS in orbit around Earth and v_2 = the speed of the ISS in the same orbit around a planet twice the mass of Earth.

$$v_o = \sqrt{\frac{Gm_E}{r}}$$
$$\Rightarrow v_{o2} = \sqrt{\frac{G(2m_E)}{r}}$$
$$= \sqrt{2} \times \sqrt{\frac{Gm_E}{r}}$$
$$= \sqrt{2} \times v_o$$

Therefore, if m_E increases to $2m_E$, then the speed would increase by a factor of $\sqrt{2}$.

$$v_2 = \sqrt{2}v$$
$$= \sqrt{2}\left(7.7 \times 10^3 \text{ m/s}\right)$$
$$= 1.1 \times 10^4 \text{ m/s}$$

Oscillatory Motion and Mechanical Waves

OSCILLATORY MOTION AND MECHANICAL WAVES

Table of Correlations				
Specific Expectation	**Practice Questions**	**Unit Test Questions**	**Practice Test 1**	**Practice Test 2**
Students will:				
D1 Describe the conditions that produce oscillatory motion.				
D1.1 describe oscillatory motion in terms of period and frequency	1	1		
D1.2 define simple harmonic motion as a motion due to a restoring force that is directly proportional and opposite to the displacement from an equilibrium position		2		23
D1.3 explain, quantitatively, the relationships among displacement, acceleration, velocity, and time for simple harmonic motion, as illustrated by a frictionless, horizontal mass-spring system or a pendulum, using the small-angle approximation	NR1, 3, 4, WR1a, WR1c, WR1d	3, NR4	NR10, NR11	
D1.4 determine, quantitatively, the relationships among kinetic, gravitational potential, and total mechanical energies of a mass executing simple harmonic motion	NR2, 2, WR1b	NR1, NR2, NR3, 4	28, NR12	NR12
D1.5 define mechanical resonance	5	5	WR2	28
D2 Describe the properties of mechanical waves and explain how mechanical waves transmit energy.				
D2.1 describe mechanical waves as particles of a medium that are moving in simple harmonic motion	8, 9	10		
D2.2 compare and contrast energy transport by matter and by waves	6	11, 12		
D2.3 define longitudinal and transverse waves in terms of the direction of motion of the medium particles in relation to the direction of propagation of the wave	10, 13	13		
D2.4 define the terms wavelength, wave velocity, period, frequency, amplitude, wave front, and ray as they apply to describing transverse and longitudinal waves	11, 12, 14	6, 7, 8	30, 31	29, 31
D2.5 describe how the speed of a wave depends on the characteristics of the medium	NR3	NR5, 9		30
D2.6 predict, quantitatively, and verify the effects of changing one or a combination of variables in the universal wave equation $v = f\lambda$	7	14, 15	NR13	32
D2.7 explain, qualitatively, the phenomenon of reflection as exhibited by mechanical waves	15		32	33
D2.8 explain, qualitatively, the conditions for constructive and destructive interference of waves and for acoustic resonance	16, 17	WR1	29, 33	34
D2.9 explain, qualitatively and quantitatively, the Doppler effect on a stationary observer of a moving source	18	NR6	34	35

OSCILLATORY MOTION AND MECHANICAL WAVES

D1.1   describe oscillatory motion in terms of period and frequency

PERIOD AND FREQUENCY IN OSCILLATORY MOTION

Any motion that moves back and forth is an oscillatory motion. A swinging gate, a pendulum, and a rocking chair are examples of oscillatory motion.

The number of complete oscillations made in one second is the frequency of the oscillation. Frequency (f) is measured in hertz (Hz) which means "per second."

The time for one complete oscillation ("there and back") is the period (T). Period is measured in seconds.

As with circular motion: $f = \dfrac{1}{T}$ and $T = \dfrac{1}{f}$

Practice Question: 1

D1.2   define simple harmonic motion as a motion due to a restoring force that is directly proportional and opposite to the displacement from an equilibrium position

SIMPLE HARMONIC MOTION AND THE RESTORING FORCE

Simple harmonic motion (SHM) is a special kind of oscillatory motion of a body about a point of equilibrium. It is caused by a force that is proportional to the particle's displacement from the equilibrium (relaxed) position. Note that the force is not constant. Also, the force is directed opposite to the displacement from the equilibrium point, and it tends to bring the body back to the equilibrium point. This force is called the restoring force and can be written algebraically as:

$$\vec{F}_s = -k\vec{x}$$

where x is the displacement from equilibrium, and k is the constant dependent on the material.

The negative sign shows that the force is directed opposite to the particle's displacement. A force of this type is called a linear restoring force.

Springs are excellent examples of simple harmonic motion. The force needed to stretch or compress a spring is proportional to the displacement of the spring, and the spring pulls or pushes back toward the equilibrium position. If you graphed the force needed to stretch a spring as a function of its displacement, it would look like the following graph.

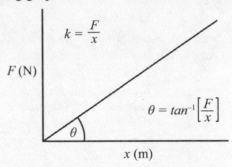

Note that the force is positive in this graph. That is because the graph is showing the force on the spring, not the force exerted by the spring.

The slope of the line is the spring constant (k). It is a measure of how strong the spring is. The spring constant is measured in N/m.

Example

A force of 100 N stretches a spring by 15.0 cm. Find the spring constant.

The magnitude of force that stretches the spring is

$F = kx$

so $k = \dfrac{F}{x}$

$ = \dfrac{100 \text{ N}}{0.150 \text{ m}}$

$ = 667 \text{ N/m}$

Example

A spring has a constant of 55 N/m. If a 1.0 kg mass is hung from this spring, how far down will it stretch?

The magnitude of the force that stretches the spring is

$$F = kx$$

$$\Rightarrow x = \frac{F}{k}$$

$$= \frac{mg}{k}$$

$$= \frac{(1.0 \text{ kg})(9.81 \text{ m/s}^2)}{55 \text{ N/m}}$$

$$= 0.18 \text{ m}$$

D1.3 explain, quantitatively, the relationships among displacement, acceleration, velocity and time for simple harmonic motion, as illustrated by a frictionless, horizontal mass-spring system or a pendulum, using the small-angle approximation

IMPORTANT VARIABLES FOR STUDYING SIMPLE HARMONIC MOTION

Simple harmonic motion can be shown by a reference circle where a particle moves at a constant speed around the circle. The x-coordinate of this particle exhibits simple harmonic motion about the origin of the graph.

Since the point's velocity consists of x- and y-components, the speed of the x-coordinate as it fluctuates about the origin varies. At maximum displacement, the x-coordinate velocity is zero and acceleration is at a maximum. At the origin though, the velocity is at a maximum and acceleration is zero.

The time for one revolution, or period, is constant, despite the variances in components of this motion.

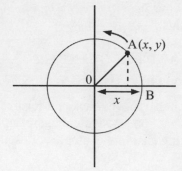

Suppose that a mass hanging on a spring is pulled upward and released. The mass will move downward past its equilibrium point until it reaches a minimum point. Then the mass will move upward to its starting point. The graph of the displacement over a few oscillations looks like this:

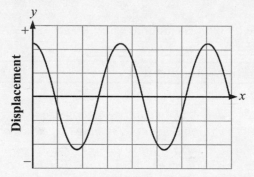

The velocity is highest at the equilibrium point and zero at the end points. The graph of the velocity looks like this:

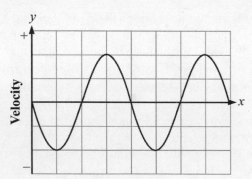

The acceleration is proportional to the force and is highest at the end points and zero at the equilibrium points. The force is in the opposite direction of the displacement. The acceleration looks like this:

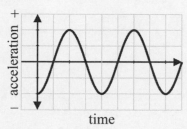

Note that the initial acceleration is negative.

When a mass on a spring exhibits simple harmonic motion, the period of the oscillation can be found with the formula:

$$T = 2\pi\sqrt{\frac{m}{k}}$$

Practice Questions: NR1, 3, 4, WR1a, WR1c, WR1d

D1.4   determine, quantitatively, the relationships among kinetic, gravitational potential and total mechanical energies of a mass executing simple harmonic motion

SIMPLE HARMONIC MOTION AND THE CONSERVATION OF MECHANICAL ENERGY

When a spring is stretched or compressed, it will store some energy. Using the conservation of energy principles, you can determine how much energy is stored by the spring.

Graphically:

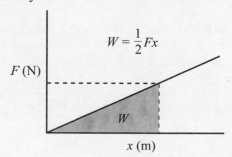

The graph shown above is a force-distance graph, so the work done stretching the spring is equal to the area under the line.

$$
\begin{aligned}
W &= \text{area} \\
&= \frac{1}{2}ab \\
&= \frac{1}{2}Fx \\
&= \frac{1}{2}(kx)x \\
&= \frac{1}{2}kx^2
\end{aligned}
$$

Since the work done on a system equals the energy gained by the system, this is the elastic potential in the spring.

Example

A spring has $k = 100$ N/m. How much energy is stored in the spring by compressing it 25.0 cm?

$$
\begin{aligned}
E_p &= \frac{1}{2}kx^2 \\
&= \frac{1}{2}(100 \text{ N/m})(0.25 \text{ m})^2 \\
&= 3.13 \text{ J}
\end{aligned}
$$

The energy of a particle in simple harmonic motion is constant throughout its motion, as long as no friction is present. Energy constantly transfers between potential and kinetic.

$$
\begin{aligned}
E_m &= E_k + E_p \\
&= \frac{1}{2}mv^2 + \frac{1}{2}kx^2
\end{aligned}
$$

At maximum displacement (maximum amplitude), velocity is zero, so there is only potential energy.

$$
\begin{aligned}
E_m &= \frac{1}{2}m(0) + \frac{1}{2}kx^2 \\
&= \frac{1}{2}kx^2
\end{aligned}
$$

At zero displacement (the origin), the velocity is at maximum. There is only kinetic energy.

$$
\begin{aligned}
E_m &= \frac{1}{2}mv^2 + \frac{1}{2}k(0)^2 \\
&= \frac{1}{2}mv^2
\end{aligned}
$$

Example

A 50.0 g mass is attached to a spring with $k = 150$ N/m. The mass is pulled 40.0 cm from the equilibrium point and then released.

a) Find its maximum speed.

The total mechanical energy is constant so:

$$\Sigma E_i = \Sigma E_f$$

For the maximum speed, consider that all of the initial potential energy is turned into kinetic energy. Therefore,

$$E_p + 0 = 0 + E_k$$

$$\frac{1}{2}kx^2 = \frac{1}{2}mv^2$$

$$\Rightarrow v = \sqrt{\frac{kx^2}{m}}$$

$$= \sqrt{\frac{(150 \text{ N/m})(0.400 \text{ m})^2}{0.0500 \text{ kg}}}$$

$$= 21.9 \text{ m/s}$$

b) Find its speed when it is 25.0 cm from the equilibrium point.

To find the speed when the mass is 25.0 cm from the equilibrium point, the potential and kinetic energies are:

$$\Sigma E_i = \Sigma E_f$$

$$E_{pi} + 0 = E_{pf} + E_{kf}$$

$$\frac{1}{2}kx_i^2 = \frac{1}{2}kx_f^2 + \frac{1}{2}mv_f^2$$

$$\Rightarrow v_f = \sqrt{\frac{kx_i^2 - kx_f^2}{m}}$$

$$= \sqrt{\frac{\begin{array}{c}(150 \text{ N/m})(0.400 \text{ m})^2 \\ -(150 \text{ N/m})(0.250 \text{ m})^2\end{array}}{0.050 \text{ kg}}}$$

$$= 17.1 \text{ m/s}$$

Another common object that moves with simple harmonic motion is a pendulum. A pendulum is powered by gravity, and it moves with simple harmonic motion for only small angles of swing (within 1% if the angle is less than 15°).

Example

A 1.00 m long pendulum is pulled back 15.0° and released. Find its maximum speed.

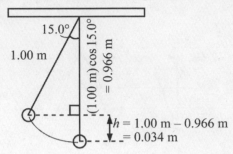

The maximum speed occurs at the bottom of the pendulum's swing.

$$\Sigma E_i = \Sigma E_f$$

$$E_p + 0 = 0 + E_k$$

$$mgh = \frac{1}{2}mv^2$$

$$\Rightarrow v = \sqrt{2gh}$$

$$= \sqrt{2(9.81 \text{ m/s}^2)(0.034 \text{ m})}$$

$$= 0.817 \text{ m/s}$$

The formula for the period of a pendulum is very similar to the equation for the period for a spring-mass system.

Period for a spring-mass system is

$$T = 2\pi\sqrt{\frac{m}{k}}$$

where m is the mass of the oscillator and k is the spring constant.

Period for a pendulum is

$$T = 2\pi\sqrt{\frac{l}{g}}$$

where l is the pendulum string length and g is the gravitational field strength.

Note that the variable for mass does not appear in the equation. This means that if you change the mass on the end of a pendulum, the period will not change.

Practice Questions: NR2, 2, WR1b

D1.5   define mechanical resonance

MECHANICAL RESONANCE

When a system is set into motion, it vibrates. If no external force is applied, this vibration occurs at some natural frequency. However, if an external force is applied in a way that complements the natural frequency, a lot of energy can transfer into the system with a small force. The effect is called resonance. For example, a singer may shatter a wine glass by singing a note that has a complementary frequency to the vibration of the glass (this has never been done without electronic amplification).

A bridge may collapse if its natural frequency is matched by that of an external force, such as wind or movement across the bridge.

A common example of resonance is when a person pushes a child on a swing. The swing has a natural frequency. If you push the swing when it reaches its maximum displacement (equal frequency), the swing goes very high with only a few pushes.

Practice Question: 5

D2.1   describe mechanical waves as particles of a medium that are moving in simple harmonic motion

D2.2   compare and contrast energy transport by matter and by waves

MECHANICAL WAVES AS A FORM OF SIMPLE HARMONIC OSCILLATION

A mechanical wave is a pattern that travels in matter. It does not consist of matter. Instead, a wave is an oscillation of matter that carries energy from one place to another. Waves travel because of the cohesive forces of the medium in which they travel. If the medium is perfectly elastic, the wave may exhibit simple harmonic motion.

This is similar to the simple harmonic motion of a particle because the magnitude of the restoring force depends on the displacement.

Suppose you want to knock down a wooden stick that is balanced on its edge. You could shoot it with a bullet or throw a ball at it. The energy used to knock down the stick is carried by the particles sent to the stick.

You could also stretch a rope past the stick and snap one end of the rope. A wave would travel through the rope, hitting the stick and knocking it over. You could focus a loud sound to knock over the stick as well. The energy used to knock down the stick is carried by different particles than the particles that were set in motion. Both of these examples show types of mechanical waves.

The source of a mechanical wave is a disturbance in the medium. This produces a pattern of waves that transmit the energy from the source to the destination.

This type of energy transmission differs from that of particle transmission. In particle transmission, a particle takes energy from the energy source to the destination. A wave uses an oscillation in the medium to transmit energy through the medium to its destination. The matter moves very little compared to the distance that the energy travels.

Practice Questions: 6, 8, 9

D2.3   define longitudinal and transverse waves in terms of the direction of motion of the medium particles in relation to the direction of propagation of the wave

TYPES OF MECHANICAL WAVES

Waves in which the particles of the medium oscillate perpendicular to the direction of the wave's movement are called transverse waves. Snapping the rope to knock down the stick would be an example.

Waves in which the particles of the medium oscillate parallel to the direction of the wave's movement are called longitudinal waves. They consist of a series of compressions and expansions of the medium in the direction of travel. This is why these waves are also called compression waves. These movements are in the same direction as the wave is moving. Sound waves are longitudinal.

Practice Questions: 10, 13

D2.4 define the terms wavelength, wave velocity, period, frequency, amplitude, wave front and ray as they apply to describing transverse and longitudinal waves

VARIABLES DESCRIBING MECHANICAL WAVES

TRANSVERSE WAVES

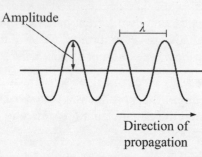

λ (lambda) = wavelength, or the length of one cycle; the distance between successive crests (or troughs)

amplitude = maximum displacement from the equilibrium position

LONGITUDINAL WAVES

λ is the distance between compressions, or rarefactions.

If you graphed the number of particles in the given volume at any point in the longitudinal wave, this becomes identical to the graph for the transverse wave.

The leading edge of the energy transport in a wave is called the wave front. To show the motion of part of a wave front, a ray or an arrow is drawn above the diagram of the wave.

Practice Questions: 11, 12, 14

D2.5 describe how the speed of a wave depends on the characteristics of the medium

D2.6 predict, quantitatively, and verify the effects of changing one or a combination of variables in the universal wave equation ($v = f\lambda$)

MECHANICAL WAVE PROPERTIES

The velocity of a wave depends on the properties of the medium through which it travels. For example, if a string has great tension, the velocity of a wave is high, as each part of the string exerts forces on their neighbouring parts. However, in a loose string, the forces between the parts of the string are less, causing a slower wave.

A wave begins when a disturbance displaces the atoms in a material away from their equilibrium position, giving them energy. The period of this disturbance propagates through the medium, transferring the energy in the form of a wave. The period of the wave is the same as the period of the source, provided dampening effects are minimized. The speed of this wave is constant for each medium.

The speed can be found with the equation: $v = f\lambda$

Example
Find the speed of a wave with a wavelength of 2.3 m and a frequency of 35 Hz.

$v = f\lambda$
$= (35\,\text{Hz})(2.3\,\text{m})$
$= (35\,\text{s}^{-1})(2.3\,\text{m})$
$= 81\,\text{m/s}$

Example
Find the speed of a wave, with a wavelength of 2.7 m and a frequency of 35 Hz.

$v = f\lambda$
$= (35\,\text{Hz})(2.7\,\text{m})$
$= (35\,\text{s}^{-1})(2.7\,\text{m})$
$= 95\,\text{m/s}$

In the above examples, you can see that the speed of the wave is directly related to the frequency and wavelength of the wave. Increasing either one of these quantities increases the speed of the wave.

If the frequency of the wave is changed within a medium, the wavelength will also change, so that the speed is unchanged.

Example

A wave has a frequency of 100 Hz and a wavelength of 2.00 m. What will be the wavelength if the frequency is reduced to 50.0 Hz?

$$v = \lambda f$$
$$= (2.00 \text{ m})(100 \text{ Hz})$$
$$= 200 \text{ m/s}$$

$$\lambda' = \frac{v}{f'}$$
$$= \frac{200 \text{ m/s}}{50.0 \text{ Hz}}$$
$$= 4.00 \text{ m}$$

Notice that halving the frequency doubled the wavelength.

When a wave moves from one medium to another, the frequency remains constant. During a medium change, speed and wavelength change to maintain frequency as a constant.

Practice Questions: 7, NR3

D2.7   explain, qualitatively, the phenomenon of reflection as exhibited by mechanical waves

REFLECTION OF MECHANICAL WAVES

When a wave hits a boundary between two media, some of the energy transmits to the new medium, and some of the energy bounces back through the original medium. The energy that bounces back through the original medium has been reflected.

There are two things to know about reflections:

Waves bounce off surfaces at the same angle at which they hit them.

Waves invert when they bounce off stiffer media or if the medium is fixed or bound so it cannot vibrate. This means that the wave is flipped over. In any wave, a crest becomes a trough, and a trough becomes a crest.

Waves do not invert if the medium is loose or unbound so it is free to vibrate during a reflection. A crest remains a crest and a trough remains a trough.

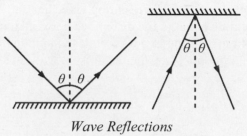

Wave Reflections

Practice Question: 15

D2.8   explain, qualitatively, the conditions for constructive and destructive interference of waves and for acoustic resonance

CONSTRUCTIVE INTERFERENCE, DESTRUCTIVE INTERFERENCE, AND ACOUSTIC RESONANCE

Waves can pass through each other. When two waves occur at the same place at the same time, interference takes place. The medium's particles move so that the energy for both waves is transferred at once.

Waves can affect each other either constructively or destructively. Constructive interference happens when both waves are in phase. This means that the crests from one wave meet the crests from the other wave, and the troughs from one wave meet the troughs from the other wave.

The medium's particles move farther than they would for either wave, which produces one larger wave with an amplitude equal to the sum of the amplitudes of the two waves.

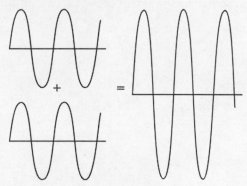

Destructive interference occurs when the waves are out of phase. This means that the crests from one wave meet the troughs from the other wave. The medium's particles move less than they would for either wave. The resulting wave has an amplitude equal to the difference between the amplitudes of the two waves. If the amplitudes are equal but opposites, the result is no wave at all.

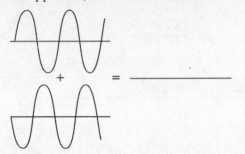

All waves can interfere. When two speakers are playing, there are often places in a room where the sound is louder due to constructive interference, and softer due to destructive interference.

When two boats pass each other, the waves left behind each create places of little wave action (destructive interference) and places with much larger waves (constructive interference).

When sound waves reflect back and forth in a musical instrument, like a horn, the waves will interfere. If the wavelength of the waves "fits" the instrument, it will form an interference pattern. This pattern will have permanent locations of constructive interference (antinodes) and destructive interference (nodes). This is called a standing wave.

Each instrument makes many different standing waves at the same time. Musicians call them harmonics. You can tell what instrument is playing because your ears can hear the different mixes of the standing waves.

Here are some possible harmonics for sound in a tube open at one end (like some flutes). In each case, a node is at the closed end and an antinode is at the open end of the tube.

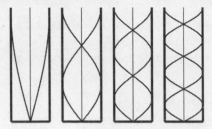

Here are some harmonics for a tube open at both ends (like a trumpet). There are antinodes at each end in this case.

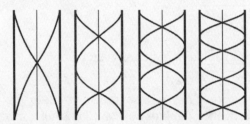

Stringed instruments make their sound differently. The waves on the strings are not sound waves, but rather are transverse waves of the strings. If their frequencies match the natural frequencies of the sound box that the strings are attached to, the sound box will resonate. The resonance frequency for open-open cylindrical tubes and string instruments can be found using $f = \dfrac{nv}{2L}$.

Where v is the speed of sound in air, L is the length of the tube, and n is the order of the corresponding resonance frequency. For example, if you were looking for the 2nd resonance frequency when 2 full wavelengths filled the tube (often called the 2nd harmonic frequency), $n = 2$.

Similarly, the resonance frequencies for an open-closed tube can be found using the equation $f = \dfrac{(2n-1)v}{2L}$.

If a wave is coming from two sources that are close together, the waves spread out from each other and interfere. If you look far enough from the sources, you can see lines of destructive and constructive interference.

This two-source interference pattern has great significance.

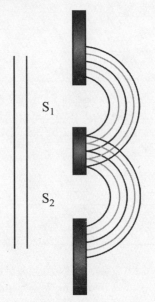

S₁

S₂

Practice Questions: 16, 17

D2.9 explain, qualitatively and quantitatively, the Doppler effect on a stationary observer of a moving source.

THE DOPPLER EFFECT

As a source of a wave moves toward a stationary observer, the observer measures a higher frequency than normal. When the source moves away from the observer, a lower frequency is measured. This is the Doppler Effect.

The frequency of a sound wave causes its pitch. The higher or lower the frequency, the higher or lower the pitch, respectively. When a sound is emitted from a moving car, the pitch is higher when it is approaching, and it lowers as it drives away.

The observed frequency of a wave is found with:

$$f' = f\left(\frac{v}{v \pm v_s}\right)$$

Where:
v_s is the speed of the source of the wave
v is the speed of the wave
f' is the observed frequency of the wave
f is the frequency of the wave emitted by the source

Example

A train whistle has a frequency of 650 Hz. The train approaches a crossing at 30.0 m/s. What frequency do the people waiting at the crossing hear? (Use $v = 340$ m/s for sound.)

Since the source (the train) is approaching, the observed frequency must be higher than 650 Hz, so you should use the minus sign in the formula.

$$f' = f\left(\frac{v}{v - v_s}\right)$$
$$= 650 \text{ Hz}\left(\frac{340 \text{ m/s}}{340 \text{ m/s} - 30.0 \text{ m/s}}\right)$$
$$= 713 \text{ Hz}$$

Example

A tuning fork moves away from an observer. It emits a 440 Hz frequency but is detected as 412 Hz. With what speed is the tuning fork moving away from the observer?

The source moves away from the observer. Therefore, use the plus sign in the formula.

$$f' = f\left(\frac{v}{v + v_s}\right)$$
$$\frac{f'}{f} = \frac{v}{v + v_s}$$
$$\frac{f}{f'} = \frac{v + v_s}{v}$$
$$\frac{fv}{f'} = v + v_s$$
$$v_s = \frac{fv}{f'} - v$$
$$= \frac{(440 \text{ Hz})(340 \text{ m/s})}{412 \text{ Hz}} - 340 \text{ m/s}$$
$$= 23.1 \text{ m/s}$$

Practice Question: 18

PRACTICE QUESTIONS—OSCILLATORY MOTION AND MECHANICAL WAVES

1. A rusty gate swings back and forth 3.0 times in 2.0 s. Its frequency is __i__ and its period is __ii__. Which of the following completes the given statement?

	i	ii
A.	3.0 Hz	2.0 s
B.	3.0 Hz	0.67 s
C.	1.5 Hz	2.0 s
D.	1.5 Hz	0.67 s

Use the following information to answer the next question.

The water mill clock in Tokyo, Japan, is the largest pendulum clock in the world.

The pendulum has a length of 22.5 m.

Numerical Response

1. The period of the pendulum is _____ seconds. (Record your answer to **three** significant digits.)

2. A pendulum that has 115 J of energy at the highest point in its swing will have _____ J of kinetic energy when its height is $\frac{1}{5}$ of its maximum possible height. (Record your answer to **three** significant digits.)

2. A 2.50 m long pendulum is pulled back to an angle of 15.0° and released. Its speed at the bottom of the swing is
   A. 1.29 m/s
   B. 1.67 m/s
   C. 6.88 m/s
   D. 7.00 m/s

CHALLENGER QUESTION

3. A spring has a constant $k = 15.0$ N/m. If a 500 g mass is hung on the spring and set into motion, the period of oscillation will be
   A. 0.188 s
   B. 0.209 s
   C. 1.15 s
   D. 36.3 s

4. A spring with $k = 60.0$ N/m has a 1.50 kg mass attached to it. The spring is compressed 0.120 m and released. The maximum speed of the mass will be
   A. 0.576 m/s
   B. 0.759 m/s
   C. 3.10 m/s
   D. 9.60 m/s

Use the following information to answer the next question.

Old fluorescent light bulbs sometimes emit an annoying buzz. The sound you hear has a frequency of 60 Hz, and is caused when the ballast in the light malfunctions.
The malfunction allows energy from the 60 Hz A.C. electricity to vibrate part of the light fixture.

5. This vibration is an example of
   A. kinetic energy
   B. thermal energy
   C. potential energy
   D. mechanical resonance

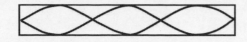

6. The diagram above illustrates standing waves
on a guitar string. The type of resonance
produced is

   A. acoustic

   B. mechanical

   C. a first harmonic

   D. a second harmonic

*Use the following information to answer
the next question.*

A tuning fork with
a frequency of
660 Hz resonates

the third harmonic frequency in an open-open
air column.

7. If the speed of sound is 343 m/s, what is the
length of the air column?

   A. 13 cm   **B.** 26 cm

   C. 43 cm   **D.** 78 cm

8. If you were able to observe a single air
molecule and follow it as a sound wave
passed, its motion could **best** be described as

   A. simple harmonic

   B. circular

   C. uniform

   D. linear

9. Which of the following characteristics does
not apply to sound waves?

   A. They transmit energy.

   B. They require a medium.

   C. They are transverse waves.

   D. They are longitudinal waves.

*Use the following diagram to answer
the next question.*

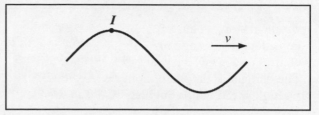

10. The diagram above illustrates a portion of a
wave travelling on a string. As the wave
moves to the right, point *I* on the string
will move

   A. up

   B. left

   C. down

   D. right

*Use the following information to answer
the next question.*

Physicists at the University of Alberta use
ultrasonic and low frequency acoustic
techniques to study the interaction of sound
waves in liquid-filled porous media. By using
piezoelectric crystals to produce different
frequencies of sound waves, the physicists can
determine how the fluid behaves within
confined spaces. The results of this research
could help predict properties, such as the
permeability of geophysical structures.

11. Compared to crystals that produce higher pitch
sounds, low-pitch crystals produce sound
waves that have a

   A. lower speed

   B. smaller period

   C. longer wavelength

   D. shorter wavelength

*Use the following information to answer
the next question.*

Tropical storms cause
considerable damage in
coastal regions every year.
The damage is caused not only
by high speed winds but also by ocean waves.

12. The energy transferred by a wave is primarily
related to its

A. speed

B. amplitude

C. frequency

D. wavelength

13. When a guitar string is plucked, the waves
produced on the string are

A. particle

B. torsional

C. transverse

D. longitudinal

14. A dog whistle emits sound at 22 000 Hz,
which is just beyond the range of human
hearing, but well within that of a dog.
This particular sound has a high

A. pitch

B. speed

C. loudness

D. wavelength

Numerical Response

3. A child utters a cry at 300 Hz. Assuming the
waves travel at 343 m/s, the wavelength of
these sound waves is _____ m. (Record
your answer to **three** significant digits.)

15. When a crest of a wave strikes a fixed end,
it gets reflected as a

A. node

B. crest

C. trough

D. supercrest

*Use the following information to answer
the next question.*

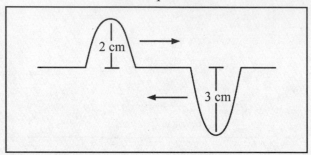

16. At complete overlap, the resultant wave pulse
will look like

A.

1 cm

B.

2 cm

C.

1 cm

D.

_____

CHALLENGER QUESTION

17. Two waves' pulses are travelling toward each other. One wave pulse has an amplitude of 3.0 cm and the other pulse has an amplitude of 7.0 mm. What will the resultant amplitude be when the two pulses interfere? (Assume pulses are the same width and are at complete overlap.)

A. 1.0×10^{-5} m

B. 2.1×10^{-4} m

C. 7.3×10^{-3} m

D. 3.7×10^{-2} m

Use the following information to answer the next two questions.

An ambulance travelling at 120 km/h is headed toward an injured person.

18. If the ambulance siren has a frequency of 800 Hz, then the frequency of sound the injured person would hear would be

A. exactly 6.70 Hz

B. exactly 800 Hz

C. lower than 6.70 Hz

D. higher than 800 Hz

Written Response

Use the following information to answer the next question.

A 2.0 kg ball is hanging from a string 0.60 m long. It is then pulled up to a height 0.20 m above the equilibrium position.

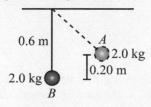

1. a) When the ball is released, what is the period of the pendulum?

b) How much energy does the ball have when it is at the height of 0.20 m?

c) What is the ball's speed at the equilibrium position?

d) What length of string must be used to have a period of 0.60 s?

ANSWERS AND SOLUTIONS—PRACTICE QUESTIONS

1. D	5. D	11. C	16. C
NR1. 9.52	6. B	12. B	17. D
NR2. 92.0	7. D	13. C	18. D
2. A	8. A	14. A	WR1. See Solution
3. C	9. C	NR3. 1.14	
4. B	10. C	15. C	

1. D

The gate swings 1.5 times in one second so the frequency is 1.5 Hz. The period is the reciprocal of this and is 0.67 s.

NR 1   9.52

$$T = 2\pi\sqrt{\frac{l}{g}}$$
$$= 2\pi\sqrt{\frac{22.5 \text{ m}}{9.81 \text{ m/s}^2}}$$
$$= 9.52 \text{ s}$$

The longer the pendulum is, the less the impact of friction and gravity (slowing the pendulum down), which affect simple harmonic motion. (If you used 3.14 for pi instead of using a π button on your calculator, your answer would be 9.51 s. Both answers would be considered to be correct.)

NR 2   92.0

At the highest point,
$$E_m = E_{p(i)} = 115 \text{ J}$$

$$\left(\text{As } E_p = mgh, \text{ then at } \frac{1}{5}h\right.$$
$$\left. E_p = \frac{1}{5}E_{p \text{ initial}} = \frac{1}{5}E_m\right)$$

$$E_p = \frac{1}{5}(115 \text{ J})$$
$$= 23.0 \text{ J}$$
$$E_k = E_m - E_p$$
$$= 115 \text{ J} - 23.0 \text{ J}$$
$$= 92.0 \text{ J}$$

E_m is the total mechanical energy which, ignoring friction, remains constant. E_p changes to E_k and then back to E_p.

2. A

$$h = 2.50 \text{ m} - (2.50 \text{ m})\cos 15.0°$$
$$h = 0.0852 \text{ m}$$
$$\Sigma E_i = \Sigma E_f$$
$$mgh = \frac{1}{2}mv^2$$
$$v = \sqrt{2gh}$$
$$= \sqrt{2(9.81 \text{ m/s})(0.0852 \text{ m})}$$
$$= 1.29 \text{ m/s}$$

3. C

$$T = 2\pi\sqrt{\frac{m}{k}}$$
$$= 2\pi\sqrt{\frac{0.500 \text{ kg}}{15.0 \text{ N/m}}}$$
$$= 1.15 \text{ s}$$

4. B

$$\Sigma E_i = \Sigma E_f$$
$$E_p = E_k$$
$$\frac{1}{2}kx^2 = \frac{1}{2}mv^2$$
$$v = \sqrt{\frac{kx^2}{m}}$$
$$= \sqrt{\frac{(60.0 \text{ N/m})(0.120 \text{ m})^2}{1.50 \text{ kg}}}$$
$$= 0.759 \text{ m/s}$$

5. D

The electric energy can transmit to metallic objects in the lamp. If the natural frequencies of the metal include 60 Hz frequencies, the metal will vibrate at that frequency.

6. B

A standing wave on a string is a type of mechanical wave since the string is undergoing oscillatory motion. The wave would not be considered acoustic since the wave is transverse and not a longitudinal compression wave. This would actually be this particular string's third harmonic since it is the third waveform that would fit between the two fixed ends of the string.

7. D

$$f = \frac{nv}{2L}$$
$$\Rightarrow L = \frac{nv}{2f}$$
$$= \frac{(3)(343 \text{ m/s})}{2(660 \text{ Hz})}$$
$$= 0.78 \text{ m}$$
$$= 78 \text{ cm}$$

The length of the column is 78 cm.

8. A

As a wave moves through a medium, particles oscillate as the energy transfers through them. Sound transmits in a longitudinal wave where the air molecules oscillate parallel to the wave's direction of travel. The air molecules move with simple harmonic motion.

9. C

Sound waves are longitudinal mechanical waves, require a medium to travel through, and transmit energy.

10. C

Point *I* will move down toward the equilibrium position, which is half way between the crest and trough.

11. C

From the formula $v = f\lambda$, a low frequency implies a larger wavelength for waves travelling at the same speed. In other words, frequency (f) and wavelength (λ) are inversely related.

12. B

The speed of a wave depends on the medium it travels through. Its frequency is determined by the source. Energy is related to the frequency and amplitude, but mostly the amplitude.

The larger the amplitude a wave has, the more work it can do.

13. C

The vibrations of the string are perpendicular to the string, so they are transverse.

14. A

The pitch is a measure of frequency. This is a musical term.

NR 3   1.14

$$\lambda = \frac{v}{f}$$
$$= \frac{343 \text{ m/s}}{300 \text{ Hz}}$$
$$= 1.14 \text{ m}$$

Note: A common error is to rearrange $v = f\lambda$ incorrectly.

15. C

A fixed-end reflection inverts the amplitude, creating a trough.

16. C

When a crest and trough overlap, destructive interference occurs.

The resulting wave has a smaller amplitude. A zero amplitude is called a node as no disturbance occurs while the waves overlap (**D**).

As the crest is shorter than the trough, the amplitude of the wave formed at overlap should be negative, but it is reduced by the crest (**C**).

$$A_R = A_1 + A_2$$
$$A_R = 2 \text{ cm} + (-3 \text{ cm})$$
$$A_R = -1 \text{ cm}$$

17. D

$$A_R = 3.0 \times 10^{-2} \text{ m} + 7.0 \times 10^{-3} \text{ m}$$
$$= 3.7 \times 10^{-2} \text{ m}$$

When two pulses overlap, they produce constructive interference, i.e., where the new amplitude is greater.

18. D

The Doppler effect is what occurs as waves become compressed due to the motion of the wave source or the observer. As the sound source moves toward you, waves arrive at your ear with an increased frequency.

The result is that the injured person would hear a higher pitch.

1. **a)** *When the ball is released, what is the period of the pendulum?*

Assume that the angle created qualifies as a small angle.

$$T = 2\pi \sqrt{\frac{l}{g}} \quad [\text{For a simple pendulum}]$$

$$= 2\pi \sqrt{\frac{0.60 \text{ m}}{9.81 \text{ m/s}^2}}$$

$$= 1.6 \text{ s}$$

b) *How much energy does the ball have when it is at the height of 0.20 m?*

$$E_p = mgh$$
$$= (2.0 \text{ kg})(9.81 \text{ m/s}^2)(0.20 \text{ m})$$
$$= 3.9 \text{ J}$$

c) *What is the ball's speed at the equilibrium position?*

E_p is measured relative to some starting point (equilibrium position). $E_p = 3.9$ J, from the previous calculation

$$E_k = \frac{1}{2}mv^2$$

$E_p = E_k$ since mechanical energy is conserved.

$$3.9 \text{ J} = \frac{1}{2}(2.0 \text{ kg})v^2$$

$$v = \sqrt{\frac{2(3.9 \text{ J})}{2.0 \text{ kg}}}$$

$$= 1.97 \text{ m/s}$$

$$= 2.0 \text{ m/s}$$

d) *What length of string must be used to have a period of 0.60 s?*

$$T = 2\pi \sqrt{\frac{l}{g}}$$

$$0.60 \text{ s} = 2\pi \sqrt{\frac{l}{9.81 \text{ m/s}^2}}$$

$$0.36 \text{ s}^2 = 4\pi^2 \frac{l}{9.81 \text{ m/s}^2}$$

$$l = \left(\frac{0.36 \text{ s}^2}{4\pi^2}\right)9.81 \text{ m/s}^2$$

$$= 0.089 \text{ m}$$

$$= 8.9 \text{ cm}$$

UNIT TEST—OSCILLATORY MOTION AND MECHANICAL WAVES

Use the following diagram to answer the next question.

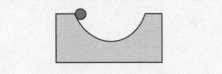

1. If the ball in the above diagram is released, it would undergo what type of motion?

   A. horizontal motion

   B. oscillatory motion

   C. uniform circular motion

   D. simple harmonic motion

2. A playground swing moves up to a height of 0.5 m from its original position. The restoring force is proportional to this distance. As the swing moves back and forth, what type of motion does it display?

   A. constant velocity

   B. linear harmonic motion

   C. uniform circular motion

   D. simple harmonic motion

Use the following information to answer the next two questions.

A group of physics students were asked to experiment with a spring found in a drawer. They hung it from a hook and added masses to it, and measured how far it stretched. Their results are shown here:

Mass (g)	100	200	300	400	500
Stretch (cm)	8.10	15.8	24.0	31.7	40.3

3. The spring constant k for this spring is

   A. 1.3×10^{-2} N/m

   B. 1.3×10^{3} N/m

   C. 12 N/m

   D. 80 N/m

CHALLENGER QUESTION

Numerical Response

1. When a 2.0 kg mass is attached to a spring hanging from a ceiling, it stretches a distance of 6.0 cm. The potential energy stored in the spring is _____ J. (Record your answer to **two** significant digits.)

Numerical Response

2. A spring is stretched by 0.683 m by a 22.6 N force. The spring constant is _____ N/m. (Record your answer to **three** significant digits.)

CHALLENGER QUESTION

Numerical Response

3. A 10 kg mass is hung from a spring with a spring constant of 14 N/m. The amount of potential energy stored in the spring is _____ kJ. (Record your answer to **two** significant digits.)

Numerical Response

4. If the spring in numerical response 3 were compressed by 3.0 cm, it would be storing $ab \times 10^{-c}$ J of energy.
   The value of abc is _____. (Record your answer as a **three-digit** number.)

CHALLENGER QUESTION

4. A device to shoot marbles is designed so that a spring with $k = 9.25$ N/m is pulled back 8.7 cm (0.087 m), and a 10.0 g (0.010 kg) marble is placed in front of it. Upon release, the spring returns halfway to its equilibrium position as it shoots the marble. The speed at which the marble is shot is

   A. 1.32 m/s   B. 1.75 m/s

   C. 2.29 m/s   D. 5.25 m/s

5. Which of the following situations is **not** an example of mechanical resonance?

   A. A violinist bowing a string.

   B. A tuning fork on a table top.

   C. A wave crashing on a shoreline.

   D. A parent pushing a child in a swing.

Use the following information to answer the next four questions.

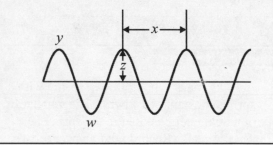

A mathematical model of a wave is shown here.

6. Locations y and w are the

   A. crest and trough

   B. period and frequency

   C. wavelength and amplitude

   D. longitudinal and transverse

7. Measurement z is the wave's

   A. energy

   B. frequency

   C. amplitude

   D. wavelength

8. The wavelength is represented by

   A. w B. x

   C. y D. z

9. If the speed of this wave is 10 m/s, its frequency would be

   A. $10xy$ B. $\dfrac{10}{z}$

   C. $\dfrac{x}{10 \text{ m/s}}$ D. $\dfrac{10 \text{ m/s}}{x}$

CHALLENGER QUESTION

Numerical Response

5. At 18.0°C, a 660 Hz sound has a wavelength of 52.0 cm. The speed of sound at that temperature is _____ m/s. (Record your answer to **three** significant digits.)

10. Two children make a crude telephone by tying a string between two tin cans and pulling it taut. When one child talks into one can, the other child can hear what her friend says in the other can. The conversation is being transmitted along the string by

    A. particle waves

    B. mechanical waves

    C. longitudinal waves

    D. electromagnetic waves

Use the following information to answer the next question.

Evacuated jars are sealed glass containers that have had all of the gases within them removed. They are curved to increase their structural strength and protect against implosive pressure.

11. If an electric bell inside an evacuated jar was turned on, the ringing of the electric bell would **not** be audible because sound waves

   A. form standing waves

   B. slow down in the glass

   C. do not travel through glass

   D. do not travel through a vacuum

CHALLENGER QUESTION

12. In which of the following situations is energy **not** transmitted by waves?

   A. A sonic boom of a jet

   B. A violin string vibrating

   C. A laser used in eye surgery

   D. A waterfall turning a generator

13. Sound waves are classified as longitudinal because the particles in the medium

   A. separate to allow a wave to pass

   B. travel along in the direction of the wave

   C. vibrate parallel to the direction of the wave

   D. vibrate perpendicular to the direction of the wave

14. Successive wave pulses are sent along a string every 1.5 s. If the time between each pulse increased to 3.0 s, then the frequency of the wave is

   A. halved

   B. doubled

   C. tripled

   D. quadrupled

15. When water waves pass from deep water to shallow water in a ripple tank, which of the following characteristics do **not** change?

   A. speed

   B. amplitude

   C. frequency

   D. wavelength

CHALLENGER QUESTION

Numerical Response

6. An ambulance siren has a frequency of 800 Hz . It is approaching to a patient at 120 km/h. Given that the speed of sound is 343 m/s, the apparent frequency heard by the injured person, assuming that he or she is stationary, is _____ Hz. (Record your answer to **three** significant digits.)

Read these two descriptions of sound resonance in an air column closed at one end before answering the following question.

a) A tuning fork is played over a tall cylinder filled with water. The level of the water is varied, and at certain depths the tuning fork's sound is amplified.

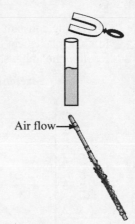

Air flow→

b) A flute is played by blowing across a hole in the side of the flute.

Written Response

1. Compare and contrast the way that sound is made to resonate in each of the two situations.

ANSWERS AND SOLUTIONS—UNIT TEST

1. B	NR4. 633	9. D	14. A
2. D	4. C	NR5. 343	15. C
3. C	5. C	10. B	NR6. 886
NR1. 0.59	6. A	11. D	WR1. See Solution
NR2. 33.1	7. C	12. D	
NR3. 0.34	8. B	13. C	

1. B

Any motion that is repetitive is considered oscillatory. Simple harmonic motion results when the restoring force is proportional to the displacement from the equilibrium position (in this case at the bottom). In this case, the restoring force is not linear, since the angle at the top is too big.

2. D

In this case, the restoring force is linear, so the motion is simple harmonic.

3. C

The spring constant is equal to the slope of a force/displacement graph. The information would result in the graph shown here.

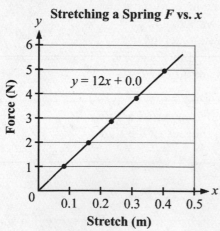

Stretching a Spring F vs. x

$y = 12x + 0.0$

$$k = \text{slope} = \frac{\text{rise}}{\text{run}}$$

$$= \frac{(0.5 \text{ kg})(9.81 \text{ m/s}^2) - (0.1 \text{ kg})(9.81 \text{ m/s}^2)}{(0.403 \text{ m} - 0.810 \text{ m})}$$

The constant is 12 N/m.

NR 1   0.59

$$\vec{F}_{net} = \vec{F}_g + \vec{F}_s$$
$$0 = m\vec{g} + (-k\vec{x})$$
$$m\vec{g} = k\vec{x}$$

Considering magnitude only

$$k = \frac{mg}{x}$$
$$= \frac{(2.0 \text{ kg})(9.81 \text{ N/kg})}{6.0 \times 10^{-2} \text{ m}}$$
$$= 327 \text{ N/m}$$

$$E_p = \frac{1}{2}kx^2$$
$$= \frac{1}{2}(327 \text{ N/m})(6.0 \times 10^{-2} \text{ m})^2$$
$$= 0.59 \text{ J}$$

NR 2   33.1

The magnitude of the force that stretches the spring is

$$F = kx$$
$$k = \frac{F}{x}$$
$$= \frac{22.6 \text{ N}}{0.683 \text{ m}}$$
$$= 33.1 \text{ N/m}$$

NR 3   0.34

Let down be the positive direction.

$$\vec{F}_{net} = \vec{F}_s + \vec{F}_g = 0$$
$$\Rightarrow \vec{F}_s = -\vec{F}_g$$
$$-k\bar{x} = -m\vec{g}$$
$$\bar{x} = \frac{m\vec{g}}{k}$$
$$\bar{x} = \frac{(10\ kg)(9.81\ m/s^2)}{14\ N/m}$$
$$\bar{x} = 7.0\ m\ downward$$

Sub the magnitude of the displacement into the elastic potential energy equation.

$$E_p = \frac{1}{2}kx^2$$
$$= \frac{1}{2}(14\ N/m)(7.0\ m)^2$$
$$= 343\ J$$
$$= 0.34\ kJ$$

NR 4   633

$$E_p = \frac{1}{2}kx^2$$
$$= \frac{1}{2}(14\ N/m)(0.030\ m)^2$$
$$= 6.3 \times 10^{-3}\ J$$

4.   C

$$\Sigma E_i = \Sigma E_f$$
$$E_{pi} = E_{pf} + E_k$$
$$\frac{1}{2}kx^2 = \frac{1}{2}kx_f^2 + E_k$$

$$\frac{1}{2}(9.25\ N/m)(0.087)^2$$
$$= \frac{1}{2}(9.25 N/m)(0.0435\ m)^2 + E_k$$
$$E_k = 0.026\ 25\ J$$
$$E_k = \frac{1}{2}mv^2$$
$$v = \sqrt{\frac{2E_k}{m}}$$
$$= \sqrt{\frac{2(0.026\ 25\ J)}{0.0100\ kg}}$$
$$= 2.29\ m/s$$

5.   C

"Waves on the shoreline" is the only example that does not involve an energy input at a specific frequency to transfer energy to an object.

Use the following illustration for the next four solutions.

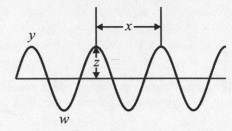

6.   A

Crests are the upward displacements in a wave model, and troughs are the downward displacements.

7.   C

Amplitude is the maximum displacement from equilibrium.

8.   B

The wavelength is the distance between two consecutive crests.

9.   D

$$v = \lambda f$$
$$f = \frac{v}{\lambda}$$
$$= \frac{10\ m/s}{x}$$

Note: When the value of x is inserted its unit will come into account (say m) and the unit of frequency becomes s^{-1} or Hz.

NR 5   343

$$v = \lambda f$$
$$= (0.520\ m)(660\ Hz)$$
$$= 343\ m/s$$

The temperature affects the speed of sound, as higher temperatures cause air molecules to vibrate faster and therefore sound waves can travel more quickly.

10. B

The sound waves are a form of mechanical waves, which cause vibrations in the string.

11. D

Sound is a mechanical wave and needs a medium to transmit through. Without a medium, sound waves cannot propagate. Therefore, sound waves do not travel through a vacuum.

12. D

Falling water turns a generator, which produces electricity. No waves are needed for this to occur.

13. C

Sound waves travel longitudinally because the particles vibrate parallel to the direction of the wave.

14. A

$$f_1 = \frac{1}{T}$$
$$= \frac{1}{1.5 \text{ s}}$$
$$= 0.67 \text{ Hz}$$
$$f_2 = \frac{1}{T}$$
$$= \frac{1}{3.0 \text{ s}}$$
$$= 0.33 \text{ Hz}$$
$$f_2 = \frac{1}{2} f_1$$

The time between pulses, or oscillations, is called the period. Another way to look at this is as the period doubled, and as T and f are inversely related, then the frequency must be half.

That is, if $f = \frac{1}{T}$, $f_1 = \frac{1}{T}$, and if f_2 has twice the period of f_1 $\left(f_2 = \frac{1}{2T} \right)$, then

$$f_2 = \frac{1}{2T}$$
$$= \frac{1}{2} \times \frac{1}{T}$$
$$= \frac{1}{2} f_1$$

15. C

Frequency is determined by the source. As a result, speed and wavelength alter to maintain f as constant. Shallow water is a slower medium, so the wave speed (v) decreases causing the wavelength (λ) to increase. This is due to the relationship $f = \frac{v}{\lambda}$.

NR 6   886

The source is moving to a stationary observer.

The observed frequency is

$$f' = f\left(\frac{v}{v - v_s} \right)$$
$$120 \text{ km/h} = 120 \text{ km/h} \times \frac{1000 \text{ m}}{1.00 \text{ km}} \times \frac{1.00 \text{ h}}{3600 \text{ s}}$$
$$= 33.3 \text{ m/s}$$
$$f' = (800 \text{ Hz})\left(\frac{(343 \text{ m/s})}{343 \text{ m/s} - 33.3 \text{ m/s}} \right)$$
$$= (800 \text{ Hz})(1.108)$$
$$= 886.4 \text{ Hz}$$
$$= 886 \text{ Hz}$$

Note: Common errors include algebra mistakes, forgetting to convert km/h into m/s, and forgetting that subtraction occurs on the denominator for an approaching source and listener.

1.

Compare and contrast the way that sound is made to resonate in each of the two situations.

When you are asked to compare and contrast something, you are to look for both similarities and differences. Both objects involve mechanical resonance in an air column that is closed on one end. The relative positions of the nodes and antinodes will be the same in both situations. The tuning fork emits only one frequency (and therefore one wavelength). In order for resonance to occur, the length of the tube must change to "fit" the waves. The changing water level accomplishes this. A flute has a constant length, so the player must produce the correct wavelengths to "fit" the tube. This is accomplished by blowing across the hole. The turbulence produced creates all frequencies. The tube causes resonance with the ones that "fit."

KEY Strategies for Success on Tests

TEST PREPARATION AND TEST-TAKING SKILLS

THINGS TO CONSIDER WHEN TAKING A TEST

* It is normal to feel anxious before you write a test. You can manage this anxiety by:
    * –Thinking positive thoughts. Imagine yourself doing well on the test.
    * –Making a conscious effort to relax by taking several slow, deep, controlled breaths. Concentrate on the air going in and out of your body.

* Before you begin the test, ask questions if you are unsure of anything.

* Jot down key words or phrases from any instructions your teacher gives you.

* Look over the entire test to find out the number and kinds of questions on the test.

* Read each question closely and reread if necessary.

* Pay close attention to key vocabulary words. Sometimes these are **bolded** or *italicized*, and they are usually important words in the question.

* If you are putting your answers on an answer sheet, mark your answers carefully. Always print clearly. If you wish to change an answer, erase the mark completely and then ensure your final answer is darker than the one you have erased.

* Use highlighting to note directions, key words, and vocabulary that you find confusing or that are important to answering the question.

* Double-check to make sure you have answered everything before handing in your test.

When taking tests, students often overlook the easy words. Failure to pay close attention to these words can result in an incorrect answer. One way to avoid this is to be aware of these words and to underline, circle, or highlight them while you are taking the test.

Even though some words are easy to understand, they can change the meaning of the entire question, so it is important that you pay attention to them. Here are some examples:

all	always	most likely	probably	best	not
difference	usually	except	most	unlikely	likely

Example

1. Which of the following equations is **not** considered abiotic?

    A. wind

    B. bacteria

    C. sunlight

    D. precipitation

HELPFUL STRATEGIES FOR ANSWERING MULTIPLE-CHOICE QUESTIONS

A multiple-choice question gives you some information, and then asks you to select an answer from four choices. Each question has one correct answer. The other answers are distractors, which are incorrect. Below are some strategies to help you when answering multiple-choice questions.

- Quickly skim through the entire test. Find out how many questions there are and plan your time accordingly.

- Read and reread questions carefully. Underline key words and try to think of an answer before looking at the choices.

- If there is a graphic, look at the graphic, read the question, and go back to the graphic. Then, you may want to underline the important information from the question.

- Carefully read the choices. Read the question first and then each answer that goes with it.

- When choosing an answer, try to eliminate those choices that are clearly wrong or do not make sense.

- Some questions may ask you to select the best answer. These questions will always include words like *best*, *most appropriate*, or *most likely*. All of the answers will be correct to some degree, but one of the choices will be better than the others in some way. Carefully read all four choices before choosing the answer you think is the best.

- If you do not know the answer, or if the question does not make sense to you, it is better to guess than to leave it blank.

- Do not spend too much time on any one question. Make a mark (*) beside a difficult question and come back to it later. If you are leaving a question to come back to later, make sure you also leave the space on the answer sheet, if you are using one.

- Remember to go back to the difficult questions at the end of the test; sometimes clues are given throughout the test that will provide you with answers.

- Note any negative words like *no* or *not* and be sure your choice fits the question.

- Before changing an answer, be sure you have a very good reason to do so.

- Do not look for patterns on your answer sheet, if you are using one.

HELPFUL STRATEGIES FOR ANSWERING OPEN-RESPONSE QUESTIONS

A written response requires you to respond to a question or directive such as **explain**, **predict**, **list**, **describe**, **show your work**, **solve**, or **calculate**. In preparing for open-response tasks you may wish to:

- Read and reread the question carefully.
- Recognize and pay close attention to directing words such as *explain*, *show your work*, and *describe*.
- Underline key words and phrases that indicate what is required in your answer, such as *explain*, *estimate*, *answer*, *calculate*, or *show your work*.
- Write down rough, point-form notes regarding the information you want to include in your answer.
- Think about what you want to say and organize information and ideas in a coherent and concise manner within the time limit you have for the question.
- Be sure to answer every part of the question that is asked.
- Include as much information as you can when you are asked to explain your thinking.
- Include a picture or diagram if it will help to explain your thinking.
- Try to put your final answer to a problem in a complete sentence to be sure it is reasonable.
- Reread your response to ensure you have answered the question.
- Think: Does your answer make sense?
- Listen: Does it sound right?
- Use appropriate subject vocabulary and terms in your response.

ABOUT SCIENCE TESTS

What You Need to Know about Science Tests

To do well on a science test, you need to understand and apply your knowledge of scientific concepts. Reading skills can also make a difference in how well you perform. Reading skills can help you follow instructions and find key words, as well as read graphs, diagrams, and tables.

Science tests usually have two types of questions: knowledge questions and skill questions. Knowledge questions test for your understanding of science ideas. Skill questions test how you would use your science knowledge.

How You Can Prepare for Science Tests

Below are some strategies that are particular to preparing for and writing science tests.

- Note-taking is a good way to review and study important information from your class notes and textbook.

- Sketch a picture of the process or idea being described in a question. Drawing is helpful for learning and remembering concepts.

- Check your answer to practice questions the require formulas by working backward to the beginning. You can find the beginning by going step-by-step in reverse order.

- When answering questions with graphics (pictures, diagrams, tables, or graphs), read the test question carefully.

  –Read the title of the graphic and any key words.
  –Read the test question carefully to figure out what information you need to find in the graphic.
  –Go back to the graphic to find the information you need.

- Always pay close attention when pressing the keys on your calculator. Repeat the procedure a second time to be sure you pressed the correct keys.

TEST PREPARATION COUNTDOWN

If you develop a plan for studying and test preparation, you will perform well on tests.

Here is a general plan to follow seven days before you write a test.

Countdown: 7 Days before the Test

1. Review the following information:
   - Areas to be included on the test

   - Types of test items

   - General and specific test tips

2. Start preparing for the test at least 7 days before the test. Develop your test preparation plan and set time aside to prepare and study.

Countdown: 6, 5, 4, 3, 2 Days before the Test

1. Review old homework assignments, quizzes, and tests.

2. Rework problems on quizzes and tests to make sure you still know how to solve them.

3. Correct any errors made on quizzes and tests.

4. Review key concepts, processes, formulas, and vocabulary.

5. Create practice test questions for yourself and then answer them. Work out many sample problems.

Countdown: The Night before the Test

1. The night before the test is for final preparation, which includes reviewing and gathering material needed for the test before going to bed.

2. Most important is getting a good night's rest and knowing you have done everything possible to do well on the test.

Test Day

1. Eat a healthy and nutritious breakfast.

2. Ensure you have all the necessary materials.

3. Think positive thoughts: "I can do this." "I am ready." "I know I can do well."

4. Arrive at your school early so you are not rushing, which can cause you anxiety and stress.

SUMMARY OF HOW TO BE SUCCESSFUL DURING A TEST

You may find some of the following strategies useful for writing a test.

- Take two or three deep breaths to help you relax.
- Read the directions carefully and underline, circle, or highlight any important words.
- Look over the entire test to understand what you will need to do.
- Budget your time.
- Begin with an easy question, or a question you know you can answer correctly, rather than following the numerical question order of the test.
- If you cannot remember how to answer a question, try repeating the deep breathing and physical relaxation activities first. Then, move on to visualization and positive self-talk to get yourself going.
- When answering a question with graphics (pictures, diagrams, tables, or graphs), look at the question carefully.
  - Read the title of the graphic and any key words.
  - Read the test question carefully to figure out what information you need to find in the graphic.
  - Go back to the graphic to find the information you need.
- Write down anything you remember about the subject on the reverse side of your test paper. This activity sometimes helps to remind you that you do know something and you are capable of writing the test.
- Look over your test when you have finished and double-check your answers to be sure you did not forget anything.

NOTES

Practice Tests

PRACTICE TEST 1

1. An example of a scalar quantity is
   A. force
   B. velocity
   C. acceleration
   D. temperature

2. A rocket sled accelerates from 5.00 m/s at a rate of 22.0 m/s^2 for 4.82 s. The distance travelled by the sled while doing this is
   A. 3.00 m
   B. 7.10 m
   C. 256 m
   D. 280 m

Use the following information to answer the next two questions.

A solar powered car being built at Queen's University will compete at the World Solar Challenge in Australia.

It is powered by a solar array that can produce 1 200 W and has a maximum velocity of 120 km/h.

3. What average acceleration would be needed to reach a velocity of 120 km/h in 60 s if the initial velocity is 30 km/h?
   A. 4.5×10^3 km/h^2
   B. 5.3×10^3 km/h^2
   C. 7.6×10^3 km/h^2
   D. 9.0×10^3 km/h^2

4. Assuming the acceleration is uniform, which of the following graphs illustrates the motion of the vehicle in the previous question?

   A.
   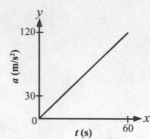

   B.
   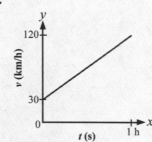

   C.
   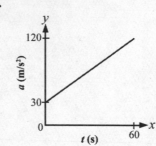

   D.
   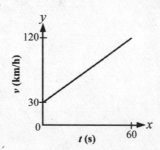

Numerical Response

1. A catapult accelerates a rock from rest to 65 m/s over the distance of 2.5 m. The rock's acceleration is $a.b \times 10^c$ m/s^2. The value of abc is ___. (Record your answer as a **three-digit** number.)

Use the following information to answer the next question.

The Mars rover was used in the summer of 1997 to explore the surface of Mars. The rover was capable of speeds up to 60 cm/min. The graph below shows a possible trip of the rover from its home base ($t = 0$ min).

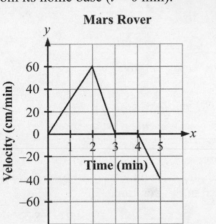

Mars Rover

5. At the end of 5.0 min, relative to its home base, the displacement of the rover is

A. 70 cm

B. 90 cm

C. 110 cm

D. 140 cm

Use the following information to answer the next two questions.

A pilot flies on a course of 23° E of N at 78 m/s. However, there is a strong wind blowing from west to east at 36 m/s.

Numerical Response

2. The magnitude of the plane's resultant velocity with respect to the ground is ___ m/s. (Record your answer as a **two-digit** number.)

6. Without calculating the approximate direction to which the pilot should head, to compensate for the wind and maintain original direction the pilot should fly a few degrees

A. S of E   B. N of E

C. N of W   D. W of N

Use the following information to answer the next two questions.

Sharks have very highly developed senses that enable them to pick up very small vibrations in the water. They are also very fast—the blue shark has been measured at speeds of 64 km/h.

7. If a blue shark, swimming east, is chasing a fish swimming at 15 km/h east, what does the motion of the fish appear to be, relative to the shark?

A. 49 km/h west   B. 49 km/h east

C. 79 km/h west   D. 79 km/h east

8. If the fish is initially 165 m from the shark, how long will it be before the shark catches the fish?

A. 0.082 s   B. 3.4 s

C. 7.5 s   D. 12 s

9. The velocity of an object at the end of each of four successive seconds is 1 m/s, 2 m/s, 4 m/s, and 8 m/s respectively. The object could best be described as moving with

A. uniform motion

B. negative acceleration

C. uniformly accelerated motion

D. non-uniformly accelerated motion

10. A mouse zigzags across a lawn. It runs 2.5 m northeast, and then 1.2 m southeast. The magnitude of the mouse's total displacement is

A. 1.3 m
B. 2.2 m
C. 2.8 m
D. 3.7 m

11. A skater moves across the ice with no change in velocity. Which statement best describes the reason that the skater's velocity is constant?

A. All the forces acting on her are balanced.

B. There is no friction on the ice slowing the skater down.

C. The skater is moving in a straight line across the ice.

D. The skater is moving in a straight line and all the forces acting on her are balanced.

12. A 7.0 N force acts on a 1.5 kg mass to give it an acceleration of 4.0 m/s^2. The force of friction, including direction, is

A. −6.0 N
B. −1.0 N
C. 1.0 N
D. 6.0 N

13. Some children are pulling a toboggan across a field at a constant speed. The net force on the toboggan is

A. zero

B. equal to the force of friction

C. larger than the force of friction

D. smaller than the force of friction

14. A 65 kg person is riding an elevator while standing on a weigh scale. If the scale reads 600 N, the acceleration of the elevator car is

A. 0.58 m/s^2 upward

B. 9.23 m/s^2 upward

C. 0.58 m/s^2 downward

D. 9.23 m/s^2 downward

Use the following information to answer the next question.

Two people push a heavy box up a ramp, as shown in the diagram.

15. If friction can be ignored between the box and the ramp, and if the force that each person exerts on the box is labelled F_{app}, the net force acting on the box parallel to the ramp is

A. $2F_{app} - mg$

B. $2F_{app} - mg\cos\theta$

C. $2F_{app} - mg\sin\theta$

D. $2F_{app} - mg\tan\theta$

Use the following information to answer the next question.

A force of 6.0 N and another force of 4.0 N act simultaneously on a body of mass 5.0 kg, as shown in the diagram.

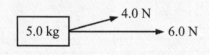

16. The magnitude of the acceleration of the body would be

A. less than 0.80 m/s^2

B. greater than 2.0 m/s^2

C. between 1.2 m/s^2 and 2.0 m/s^2

D. between 0.80 m/s^2 and 1.2 m/s^2

Numerical Response

3. The coefficient of static friction between someone's shoes and a freshly waxed floor is 0.22. The force needed to make a 45 kg person slide across the floor is ___ N. (Record your answer to **two** significant digits.)

4. One of the tallest roller coasters in the world is the 77.7 m high Fujiyama in Japan. If a car has a speed of 0.50 m/s when it reaches the top of the drop and a speed of 38 m/s at the bottom of the drop, the magnitude of the net force acting on a 250 kg loaded car if the first drop is at an angle of 65° below horizontal is _____ kN. (Record your answer to **two** significant digits.)

17. A force of 30 N acts at 40° to the horizontal. What is the acceleration on an 86 kg mass on a horizontal surface if the force of friction is 25 N?

   A. 0.64 m/s^2

   B. 0.023 m/s^2

   C. 0.0058 m/s^2

   D. 0 m/s^2

18. The path of a projectile near the surface of Earth is

   A. circular

   B. periodic

   C. elliptical

   D. parabolic

Numerical Response

5. A golf ball on the ground is struck and begins travelling at an angle of 40.0° to the horizontal at a speed of 45.7 m/s. Ignoring any resistance and lift (both of which are significant), and assuming the ground is level, the maximum horizontal distance travelled by the ball, expressed in scientific notation, is $a.bc \times 10^d$ m. The value of *abcd* is _____. (Record your answer as a **four-digit** number.)

6. Car I is travelling at 30 m/s when it locks its brakes and slides to a stop. Car II is travelling at 10 m/s when it locks its brakes and slides to a stop. Assuming both cars are identical, how many times farther will car I slide than car II? ____ times

19. The first power station built to harness the power of ocean tides opened on November 26, 1966, on the Rance estuary in France. The station converted tidal energy into 2.4 MW of electrical power. How much work does this station do in one day?

   A. 2.8×10^3 J   **B.** 2.4×10^8 J

   C. 2.1×10^{10} J   **D.** 2.1×10^{11} J

20. Sally pushes a 100 kg refrigerator 1.30 m across the kitchen floor with a force of 125 N. The work she did on the fridge is

   A. 130 J   **B.** 163 J

   C. 130 N   **D.** 163 N

21. A 20.0 g bullet is shot vertically upward. It has 3.6×10^3 J of kinetic energy as it leaves the gun. How high above the gun will the bullet rise if air resistance is ignored?

   A. 3.0×10^1 m

   B. 3.0×10^2 m

   C. 1.8×10^4 m

   D. 1.8×10^5 m

Use the following information to answer the next question.

The Mindbender rollercoaster in the West Edmonton Mall amusement park is not only the world's largest indoor rollercoaster (height of 43.5 m), but is also the one that exerts the largest "g-force" of 6.5 when travelling at a speed of 88 km/h through a loop. A "g-force" of 6.5 means 6.5 times the acceleration due to gravity.

Numerical Response

7. The radius of the loop is _____ m. (Record your answer to **two** significant digits.)

Use the following information to answer the next question.

Information is stored on the surface of compact discs in a series of ridges and flat regions that can be read using a laser. The discs have a diameter of 12.0 cm and rotate at 500 rpm.

22. Find the force of friction needed to keep a coin ($m = 10$ g), placed on the disc 6.0 cm from centre, from sliding off the rotating disc.

   A. 0.098 N

   B. 1.6 N

   C. 3.3 N

   D. 41 N

Numerical Response

8. A brick is thrown through the air at 6.00 m/s. If its kinetic energy is 55.0 J, then its mass is _____ kg. (Record your answer to **three** significant digits.)

Use the following information to answer the next two questions.

In chemistry, a centrifuge may be used to separate substances. Test tubes with mixtures in them are placed in a circular disk that is rotated at a high speed. The heavier substances are then forced to the bottom of the tube.

23. If the disk has a radius of 10 cm and is rotated at 1 000 rev/s, then the speed of the test tubes is

   A. 6.3×10^{-4} m/s   **B.** 1.0×10^2 m/s

   C. 1.0×10^3 m/s   **D.** 6.3×10^2 m/s

24. The centripetal force on the test tube is provided by

   A. motor

   B. gravity

   C. friction

   D. tension in the disk

25. A physics student swings a 1.50 kg bucket of water on the end of a string 0.800 m long in a vertical circle. If the speed of the bucket is 6.00 m/s at the top of the circle, what is the tension in the string?

   A. 14.7 N   **B.** 52.8 N

   C. 67.5 N   **D.** 82.2 N

26. Astronauts who spend a considerable length of time in a space station, such as the astronauts who stayed in MIR, are noticeably taller (by several centimetres) when they return to Earth. The reason for this is that in a space station

   A. there is a lack of inertia

   B. the force of gravity is almost zero

   C. there is no external support force acting on the astronauts

   D. the gravitational force is cancelled out by the centripetal force

Numerical Response

9. A space shuttle is 400 km above Earth's surface. The orbital period of the shuttle around Earth is $abc \times 10^d$ s . The values of a, b, c and d are, respectively, _____. (Record your answer as a **four-digit** number.)

27. The gravitational constant, G, in Newton's law of universal gravitation is an extremely small number: 6.67×10^{-11} N·m²/kg² . What is the reason that the gravitational force is the most significant force for understanding the shape and size of the universe?

   A. The universe is very large.

   B. The universe is mostly empty space.

   C. Everything in the universe has a mass.

   D. Masses of objects in the universe are very large.

Numerical Response

10. A 75.0 N force compresses a spring by 0.150 m. The spring constant for this spring is _____ N/m. (Record your answer to **three** significant digits.)

11. In order for the pendulum of a clock to have a period of 1.00 seconds, the pendulum must be _____ cm long. (Record your answer to **three** significant digits.)

Use the following information to answer the next two questions.

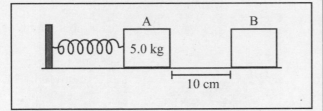

28. When the 5.0 kg mass in the above diagram is pulled out from position A (equilibrium position) to position B, 20 J of potential energy is stored in the spring. What is the spring constant?

    A. 0.20 kN/m

    B. 0.40 kN/m

    C. 2.0 kN/m

    D. 4.0 kN/m

Numerical Response

12. When the 5.0 kg block is released, the maximum speed of the mass will be _____ m/s. (Record your answer to **two** significant digits.)

29. In older vehicles, it is common for rattles and squeaks to develop. Very often, a particular vibration will become very obvious at a certain speed, but not at slightly lower or slightly higher speeds. This is an example of

    A. interference

    B. the Doppler effect

    C. mechanical resonance

    D. simple harmonic motion

Use the following graph to answer the next question.

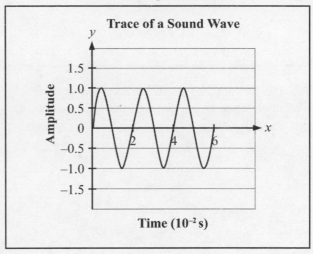

30. The frequency of this sound wave is

    A. 0.50 Hz

    B. 1.0 Hz

    C. 50 Hz

    D. 100 Hz

Use the following information to answer the next two questions.

In a wave pool, the waves are created by a mechanical arm that moves up and down in the water.

31. If the arm completes one cycle in 2.2 s, what is the frequency of the waves?

    A. 0.45 Hz

    B. 0.90 Hz

    C. 1.1 Hz

    D. 2.2 Hz

Numerical Response

13. If the wavelength of the waves in the pool is 9.0 m, then the speed of the waves is _____ m/s. (Record your answer correct to **two** significant digits.)

Use the following diagram to answer the next question.

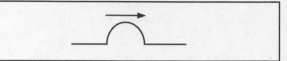

32. If a wave along a string moves toward a free unattached end, what will the reflected wave look like?

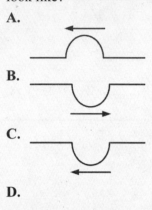

A.

B.

C.

D.

33. Waves have the ability to pass through one another. When this occurs, the waves will

   A. reflect   B. diffract

   C. transmit   D. interfere

Use the following information to answer the next question.

Radar guns are used by police to determine if a vehicle is speeding. Radar waves are emitted from the gun at a particular frequency and reflect off the vehicle back to the radar unit. The reflected wave comes back as if the moving vehicle emitted the wave in the first place.

34. If a radar gun emits waves at a frequency of 500 Hz and a vehicle is approaching the radar unit, the frequency of the reflected wave could be

   A. 451 Hz

   B. 465 Hz

   C. 495 Hz

   D. 549 Hz

Use the following information to answer the next two questions.

A breakwater is a solid barrier placed out in the water to protect beaches and harbours from the impact of waves.

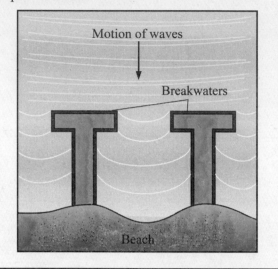

35. Water waves that occur between the breakwater and the beach are because of

   A. reflection

   B. refraction

   C. diffraction

   D. interference

36. The waves that occur between the breakwater and the beach cause very little erosion of the beach. This is due to a reduction in the wave's

   A. speed

   B. amplitude

   C. frequency

   D. wavelength

Written Response

Use the following information to answer the next question.

The movies *Deep Impact* and *Armageddon* revived concerns about the possible impact of an asteroid on Earth. If an asteroid appears to be on a collision course with Earth, it will be essential to determine the mass and velocity of the asteroid before any action is taken.

1. One possible way to obtain this information would be to send an unmanned space probe to approach, orbit, and land on the asteroid.

a) The probe could be placed in orbit around the asteroid. Describe, in general, how the orbit of the probe would be useful in determining the mass of the asteroid.

b) After the probe landed, what remote experiment could be easily done to obtain evidence that can be used, along with the mass of the asteroid, to calculate its average radius?

Include a brief design and any equations necessary for all calculations.

2. A group of physics students are experimenting with sound waves. They attach an electronic sound generator to two speakers, as shown.

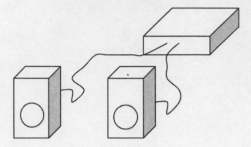

They are looking to find places in the room where constructive and destructive interference of the sound waves occurs.

a) They need a wavelength of 0.950 m so their ears can detect these locations. If the speed of sound in the room is 343 m/s, what frequency should they use?

b) How can the students tell if they found one of the locations they are looking for?

c) Make a diagram that shows where a location of constructive interference might be. Explain why you think it might be there.

ANSWERS AND SOLUTIONS—PRACTICE TEST 1

1. D	12. B	21. C	NR12. 2.8
2. D	13. A	NR7. 9.3	29. C
3. B	14. C	22. B	30. C
4. D	15. C	NR8. 3.06	31. A
NR1. 852	16. C	23. D	NR13. 4.1
5. A	NR3. 97	24. D	32. A
NR2. 98	NR4. 2.1	25. B	33. D
6. D	17. D	26. C	34. D
7. A	18. D	NR9. 5543	35. C
8. D	NR5. 2102	27. D	36. B
9. D	NR6. 3	NR10. 500	WR1. See Solution
10. C	19. D	NR11. 24.8	WR2. See Solution
11. D	20. B	28. D	

1. D

A scalar quantity has only magnitude, but no direction.

Temperature is the only choice that has no direction as a component of its measurement.

2. D

$$d = v_i t + \frac{1}{2} a t^2$$
$$= 5.00 \text{ m/s}(4.82 \text{ s}) + \frac{1}{2}(22.0 \text{ m/s}^2)(4.82 \text{ s})^2$$
$$= 280 \text{ m}$$

3. B

$$\vec{a} = \frac{\Delta \vec{v}}{t}$$
$$t = 60 \text{ s} \times \frac{1 \text{ h}}{3\,600 \text{ s}}$$
$$= 1.7 \times 10^{-2} \text{ h}$$
$$\vec{a} = \frac{\vec{v}_f - \vec{v}_i}{t}$$
$$= \frac{120 - 30 \text{ km/h}}{1.7 \times 10^{-2} \text{ h}}$$
$$= +5.3 \times 10^3 \text{ km/h}^2$$

4. D

Acceleration is given by the car's velocity over a given period of time. Plotting this would result in a graph having velocity as the y-axis and time as the x-axis, therefore graphs **A** and **C** are incorrect.

Since it only takes 60 s, not 1 h, for the car to reach its maximum velocity of 120 km/h, graph **B** is also wrong.

The uniform acceleration of the solar car gives the straight-line v–t graph shown in **D**.

NR 1   852

$$a = \frac{v_f^2 - v_i^2}{2d}$$
$$= \frac{(65 \text{ m/s})^2 - 0}{2(2.5 \text{ m})}$$
$$= 845 \text{ m/s}^2$$
$$= 8.5 \times 10^2 \text{ m/s}^2$$

5. A

The displacement is the area between the line created by a v–t graph and the x-axis.

This area can have either a positive or a negative value depending on the direction of travel. The net value is the overall displacement from the original position.

$$\bar{d} = \frac{1}{2}bh + \frac{1}{2}bh - \frac{1}{2}bh$$
$$= \frac{1}{2}(3 \text{ min})\left(60 \frac{\text{cm}}{\text{min}}\right) + \frac{1}{2}(1 \text{ min})\left(0 \frac{\text{cm}}{\text{min}}\right)$$
$$- \frac{1}{2}\left(40 \frac{\text{cm}}{\text{min}}\right)$$
$$= 90 \text{ cm} + 0 \text{ cm} - 20 \text{ cm}$$
$$= 70 \text{ cm}$$

NR 2   98

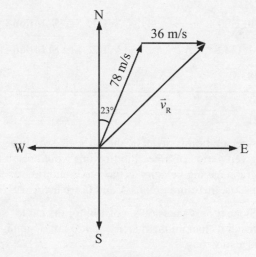

Components of the plane's velocity.
$$v_E = 78 \text{ m/s} \times \sin 23°$$
$$= 30.5 \text{ m/s}$$
$$\therefore \vec{v}_E = 30.5 \text{ m/s east}$$
$$v_N = 78 \text{ m/s} \times \cos 23°$$
$$= 71.8 \text{ m/s}$$
$$\therefore \vec{v}_N = 71.8 \text{ m/s north}$$
$$\text{total } \vec{v}_E \text{ components} = 30.5 \text{ m/s east} + 36 \text{ m/s east}$$
$$= 66.5 \text{ m/s east}$$
$$\text{total } \vec{v}_N \text{ component} = 71.8 \text{ m/s north}$$

The magnitude of the resultant velocity is
$$v_R = \sqrt{(66.5 \text{ m/s})^2 + (71.8 \text{m/s})^2}$$
$$= 98 \text{ m/s}$$

6. D

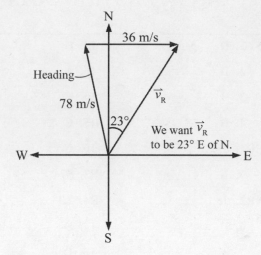

7. A

From the point of view (reference frame) of the shark, it appears that the fish is approaching it at $(64 - 15)$ km/h.

Therefore, the motion of the fish appears to be 49 km/h west.

8. D

The relative speed of the blue shark with respect to the fish is
$$v = \frac{49 \text{ km}}{1 \text{ h}} \times \frac{1\,000 \text{ m}}{1 \text{ km}} \times \frac{1 \text{ h}}{3\,600 \text{ s}}$$
$$= 13.6 \text{ m/s}$$

$$\text{speed } v = \frac{d}{t}$$
$$t = \frac{165 \text{ m}}{13.6 \text{ m/s}}$$
$$= 12 \text{ s}$$

9. D

The velocity of the object did not increase uniformly and can, therefore, be described as non-uniformly accelerated.

10. C

The displacement vectors make a right triangle, so you can use the Pythagorean theorem.

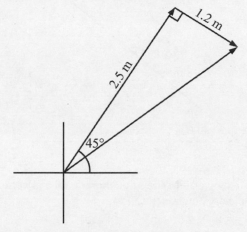

The magnitude of resultant displacement is

$$d = \sqrt{(2.5 \text{ m})^2 + (1.2 \text{ m})^2}$$
$$= 2.8 \text{ m}$$

11. D

As there is no change in velocity, the skater's acceleration is zero. Since $\vec{F}_{net} = m\vec{a}$ with $\vec{a} = 0$, then the net force acting on the skater is zero. As well, because velocity is a vector, a change in direction would imply a change in velocity.

These being true, the skater must be moving in a straight line across the ice with all forces balanced.

12. B

The applied force minus the force of friction results in an acceleration.

$$\vec{F}_{net} = m\vec{a}$$
$$= (1.5 \text{ kg})(4.0 \text{ m/s}^2)$$
$$= 6.0 \text{ N}$$
$$\vec{F}_{net} = \vec{F}_a + \vec{F}_f$$
$$6.0 \text{ N} = 7.0 \text{ N} + \vec{F}_f$$
$$\vec{F}_f = -1.0 \text{ N}$$

Recall that friction always opposes the direction of motion.

13. A

The net force is zero because that toboggan is not accelerating.

$$\vec{F} = m\vec{a}$$

14. C

$$\vec{F}_{net} = \vec{F}_N + \vec{F}_g$$
$$\vec{F}_{net} = m\vec{a}$$
$$m\vec{a} = \vec{F}_N + \vec{F}_g$$
$$\vec{a} = \frac{\vec{F}_N + m\vec{g}}{m}$$
$$= \frac{600 \text{ N} + 65 \text{ kg}(-9.81 \text{ m/s}^2)}{65 \text{ kg}}$$
$$= \frac{600 \text{ kg} \cdot \text{m/s}^2 - 637.7 \text{ kg} \cdot \text{m/s}^2}{65 \text{ kg}}$$
$$= -0.58 \text{ m/s}^2$$

Negative acceleration is downward.

15. C

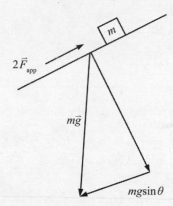

$$\vec{F}_{net} = 2\vec{F}_{app} + \vec{F}_{g\parallel}$$

Considering only magnitude

$$F_{net} = 2F - mg\sin\theta$$

16. C

The net force would be less than 10.0 N but greater than 6.0 N. This is because the net force will have to be less than the sum of the two forces if they were both acting horizontally, but greater than the 6.0 N force acting alone.

$$\vec{a} = \frac{\vec{F}_{net}}{m}$$
$$= \frac{10.0 \text{ N}}{5.0 \text{ kg}}$$
$$= 2.0 \text{ m/s}^2$$
$$\vec{a} = \frac{\vec{F}_{net}}{m}$$
$$= \frac{6.0 \text{ N}}{5.0 \text{ kg}}$$
$$= 1.2 \text{ m/s}^2$$

Therefore, the acceleration must be between 1.2 m/s² and 2.0 m/s².

NR 3   97

$$F_f = \mu F_N$$
$$= 0.22(45 \text{ kg})(9.81 \text{ m/s}^2)$$
$$= 97 \text{ N}$$

NR 4   2.1

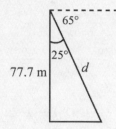

First determine the distance over which the acceleration acted.

$$\cos 25° = \frac{77.7 \text{ m}}{d}$$
$$d = \frac{77.7 \text{ m}}{\cos 25°}$$
$$= 85.73 \text{ m}$$

Now the acceleration along the slope can be calculated

$$v_f^2 = v_i^2 + 2ad$$
$$a = \frac{v_f^2 - v_i^2}{2d}$$
$$= \frac{(38 \text{ m/s})^2 - (0.50 \text{ m/s})^2}{2(85.73 \text{ m})}$$
$$= 8.42 \text{ m/s}^2$$

Magnitude of the net force is
$$F_{net} = ma$$
$$= (250 \text{ kg})(8.42 \text{ m/s}^2)$$
$$= 2\,105 \text{ N}$$
$$= 2.1 \text{ kN}$$

17. D

The horizontal component of the applied force is $30 \text{ N} \times \cos 40° = 23 \text{ N}$.

Since the applied force is less than friction, no movement will occur.

18. D

An acceleration in the vertical direction and no acceleration in the horizontal direction yields a parabolic path.

NR 5   2102

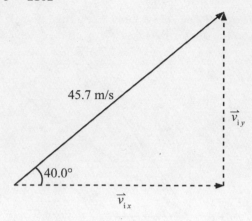

First, determine the initial horizontal and vertical velocity components.

$$v_{ix} = v \cos\theta$$
$$= (45.7 \text{ m/s})\cos 40.0°$$
$$= 35.01 \text{ m/s}$$
$$v_{iy} = v \sin\theta$$
$$= (45.7 \text{ m/s})\sin 40.0°$$
$$= 29.38 \text{ m/s}$$

Note: The vertical displacement is zero when it lands.

$$\vec{d}_y = \vec{v}_{iy}t + \frac{1}{2}\vec{g}t^2$$
$$0 = (29.37 \text{ m/s})t + \frac{1}{2}(-9.81 \text{ m/s}^2)t^2$$
$$t = \frac{2(29.37 \text{ m/s})}{9.81 \text{ m/s}^2}$$
$$= 5.988 \text{ s}$$
$$\vec{d}_x = \vec{v}_{ix}t$$
$$= (35.01 \text{ m/s})(5.988 \text{ s})$$
$$= 210 \text{ m}$$
$$= 2.10 \times 10^2 \text{ m}$$

NR 6   3

The equation $\vec{d} = \vec{v}_i t + \frac{1}{2}\vec{a}t^2$ shows that $d \propto v_i$.

Therefore, if the car is travelling three times faster, it should slide three times as far.

19. D

$$W = Pt$$
$$= (2.40 \times 10^6 \text{ J/s})\left(24 \text{ h} \times \frac{3\,600 \text{ s}}{1 \text{ h}}\right)$$
$$= 2.1 \times 10^{11} \text{ J}$$

20. B

$$W = Fd$$
$$= 125 \text{ N} \times 1.30 \text{ m}$$
$$= 163 \text{ J}$$

21. C

$$\text{max } E_p = \text{max } E_k$$
$$= 3.6 \times 10^3 \text{ J}$$
(Assuming a conservative system.)

$$3.6 \times 10^3 \text{ J} = mgh$$
$$3.6 \times 10^3 \text{ J} = (0.0200 \text{ kg})(9.81 \text{ m/s}^2)h$$
$$h = 1.8 \times 10^4 \text{ m}$$

NR 7   9.3

$$v = 88 \text{ km/h} \times \frac{1\,000 \text{ m}}{1 \text{ km}} \times \frac{1 \text{ h}}{3\,600 \text{ s}}$$
$$= 24.4 \text{ m/s}$$
$$a_c = \frac{v^2}{r}$$
$$r = \frac{v^2}{a_c}$$
$$= \frac{(24.4 \text{ m/s})^2}{(6.5)(9.81 \text{ m/s}^2)}$$
$$= 9.3 \text{ m}$$

22. B

500 rpm = 500 revolution in one minute
1 revolution = $2\pi r$

$$v = \frac{d}{t}$$
$$= \frac{500(2\pi r)}{1 \text{ min}}$$
$$= \frac{500(2\pi)(6.0 \times 10^{-2} \text{ m})}{60 \text{ s}}$$
$$= 3.14 \text{ m/s}$$

For the coin to not move
$$F_f = F_c$$
$$F_c = \frac{mv^2}{r}$$
$$= \frac{(0.010 \text{ kg})(3.14 \text{ m/s})^2}{6.0 \times 10^{-2} \text{ m}}$$
$$= 1.6 \text{ N}$$

Therefore the magnitude of $\vec{F}_f$ must equal at least 1.6 N.

NR 8   3.06

$$E_k = \frac{1}{2}mv^2$$
$$m = \frac{2E_k}{v^2}$$
$$= \frac{2(55.0 \text{ J})}{(6.00 \text{ m/s})^2}$$
$$= 3.06 \text{ kg}$$

23. D

The distance is the circumference of the disk, and the time is the period for one revolution.

$$T = \left(\frac{1}{1\,000}\right) \text{s}$$
$$v = \frac{2\pi r}{T}$$
$$= \frac{2\pi(0.10 \text{ m})}{\frac{1}{1\,000} \text{ s}}$$
$$= 6.3 \times 10^2 \text{ m/s}$$

24. D

Think of the disk as a closely-packed circular arrangement of hollow rods with a test tube at the end of each imaginary rod.

Each rod acts like a string whirling a mass. The tension is responsible for the pull or force on the test tube.

25. B

$$\vec{F}_{net} = \vec{F}_T + \vec{F}_g$$
$$\vec{F}_{net} = \vec{F}_c$$
Considering magnitudes only.
$$F_c = ma_c$$
$$= \frac{mv^2}{r}$$
$$\therefore \frac{mv^2}{r} = F_T + mg$$
$$\Rightarrow F_T = \frac{mv^2}{r} - mg$$
$$= 1.50 \text{ kg}\left(\frac{(6.00 \text{ m/s})^2}{0.800 \text{ m}} - 9.81 \text{ m/s}^2\right)$$
$$= 52.8 \text{ N}$$

26. C

Even at the altitude of the space station, there is still an appreciable gravitational field. (Keep in mind that gravity keeps the space station in orbit around Earth.)

The astronauts and the space station are not weightless but are essentially in a "free fall." Therefore, the weight of the astronauts is not supported by the space station.

Gravity, in opposition to the support/reactive forces on Earth, causes the compression of the human spinal column and joints. The absence of a support force allows these body parts to uncompress.

This variability in height is also seen in the morning when people are slightly taller than they are at the end of the day. However, this change is not detectable by the naked eye.

NR 9   5543

The gravitational force on the shuttle is the net centripetal force.

$$\vec{F}_c = \vec{F}_g$$

Considering magnitudes only.

$$\frac{4\pi^2 \not m_s r}{T^2} = \frac{Gm_E \not m_s}{r^2}$$

$$T^2 = \frac{4\pi^2 r^3}{Gm_E}$$

$$T = \sqrt{\frac{4\pi^2 \left(6.37\times10^6 \text{ m} + 4.00\times10^5 \text{ m}\right)^3}{6.67\times10^{-11} \dfrac{\text{N}\cdot\text{m}^2}{\text{kg}^2} \times 5.98\times10^{24} \text{ kg}}}$$

$$= 5.54\times10^3 \text{ s}$$

27. D

Although the constant is small, the masses of even relatively small objects, such as the moon (10^{22} kg) and Earth (10^{24} kg), are fantastically larger than the constant. Therefore, very large forces result.

NR 10   500

The magnitude of the force that compresses the spring is

$$F = kx$$

$$k = \frac{F}{x}$$

$$= \frac{75.0 \text{ N}}{0.150 \text{ m}}$$

$$= 500 \text{ N/m}$$

NR 11   24.8

$$T = 2\pi\sqrt{\frac{l}{g}}$$

$$l = \frac{gT^2}{4\pi^2}$$

$$= \frac{\left(9.81 \text{ m/s}^2\right)\left(1.00 \text{ s}\right)^2}{4\pi^2}$$

$$= 0.248 \text{ m} = 24.8 \text{ cm}$$

28. D

$$E_p = \frac{1}{2}kx^2$$

$$20 \text{ J} = \frac{1}{2}k\left(0.10 \text{ m}\right)^2$$

$$k = \frac{2\left(20 \text{ J}\right)}{\left(0.10 \text{ m}\right)^2}$$

$$= 4.0\times10^3 \text{ N/m}$$

$$= 4.0 \text{ kN/m}$$

NR 12   2.8

$$\max E_k = \max E_p$$

(assuming a closed system)

$$\frac{1}{2}mv^2 = 20 \text{ J}$$

$$\frac{1}{2}\left(5.0 \text{ kg}\right)v^2 = 20 \text{ J}$$

$$v = 2.8 \text{ m/s}$$

29. C

At a certain velocity, the car's vibration and the particular vibration achieve a frequency that causes mechanical resonance. The natural frequency of vibration of the loose car parts matches the vibrations from the road.

30. C

The period is about 0.020 s. The frequency is

$$f = \frac{1}{T}$$

$$= \frac{1}{0.020 \text{ s}}$$

$$= 50 \text{ Hz}$$

31. A

$$f_{\text{source}} = f_{\text{waves}}$$
$$f = \frac{1}{T}$$
$$= \frac{1}{2.2 \text{ s}}$$
$$= 0.45 \text{ s}^{-1} \text{ or } 0.45 \text{ Hz}$$

NR 13   4.1

$$v = \lambda f$$
$$= (9.0 \text{ m})(0.45 \text{ Hz})$$
$$= 4.1 \text{ m/s}$$

32. A

A free-end reflection does not invert, as in diagram **A**. (A fixed-end reflection does invert, as in diagram **C**.) Diagram **B** shows the reflection moving in the wrong direction while diagram **D** shows no reflection, both of which would not occur in a free-end reflection.

33. D

Waves passing through one another cause interference, which can be either destructive or constructive.

34. D

According to the Doppler Effect, the wavelengths of the reflected waves are compressed (smaller λ). Because the speed of sound remains constant, a smaller λ means a larger f ($v = f\lambda =$ constant). Therefore the frequency of the reflected wave would be greater than 500 Hz.

35. C

The bending of water waves around sharp edges is due to diffraction.

36. B

The amplitude of a wave measures its energy. Energy transfer from waves to the shore is impeded by the breakwater as it absorbs much of the initial wave energy. Thus, the amplitude of waves reaching the shore is much less. Therefore, little erosion occurs because the waves do not have much energy.

1.   **a)** *The probe could be placed in orbit around the asteroid. Describe, in general, how the orbit of the probe would be useful in determining the mass of the asteroid.*

Once the probe went into orbit around the asteroid, its period and radius of orbit could be measured. By setting the gravitational force equal to the centripetal force, the mass of the asteroid can be calculated.

$$\frac{Gm_{\text{p}}m_{\text{a}}}{r^2} = \frac{4\pi^2 m_{\text{p}} r}{T^2}$$
$$m_{\text{a}} = \frac{4\pi^2 r^3}{GT^2}$$

   b) *After the probe landed, what remote experiment could be easily done to obtain evidence that can be used, along with the mass of the asteroid, to calculate its average radius?*

Once the probe has landed on the asteroid, an experiment could be done to measure the acceleration of gravity there.

$$g = \frac{Gm_{\text{a}}}{r^2}$$
$$r = \sqrt{\frac{Gm_{\text{a}}}{g}}$$

One way to measure this acceleration would be to determine the flight time of an object that falls a known distance from rest.

$$d = \cancel{v_i t} + \frac{1}{2}gt^2$$
$$g = \frac{2d}{t^2}$$

2. **a)** *If the speed of sound in the room is 343 m/s, what frequency should they use?*

$$v = \lambda f$$
$$f = \frac{v}{\lambda}$$
$$= \frac{343 \text{ m/s}}{0.950 \text{ m}}$$
$$= 361 \text{ Hz}$$

b) *How can the students tell if they found one of the locations they are looking for?*

When they reach one of the places where constructive interference occurs, the sound from the speakers should be louder than normal. At locations of destructive interference, the sound should be softer than normal. Searching for the loudest and quietest locations would locate points of maximum constructive and destructive interference, respectively.

c) *Make a diagram that shows where a location of constructive interference might be. Explain why you think it might be there.*

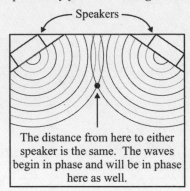

The distance from here to either speaker is the same. The waves begin in phase and will be in phase here as well.

Any location whose distance from each of the speakers is equal to a whole number of the wavelengths of the waves is a location where constructive interference occurs.

PRACTICE TEST 2

1. The difference between vectors and scalars is that vectors

 A. are negative while scalars are positive

 B. point in the opposite direction to scalars

 C. have direction while scalars have no direction

 D. are used for forces and scalars for motion

Use the following information to answer the next three questions.

The highest waterfall in the world, Angel Falls in south eastern Venezuela, has a vertical drop of 807 m.

Numerical Response

1. If the water takes 14 s to reach the bottom of the falls, its average vertical velocity is _____ m/s. (Record your answer to **two** significant digits.)

2. Ignoring the effects of air resistance, the water dropping over Angel Falls has both

 A. constant velocity and variable acceleration

 B. variable velocity and variable acceleration

 C. constant velocity and constant acceleration

 D. variable velocity and constant acceleration

3. If the water is already moving at 4.0 m/s at the top of the falls, the total mechanical energy of 10 kg of water at the top of the falls is

 A. 79 J   B. 80 J

 C. 79 kJ   D. 80 kJ

Use the following information to answer the next two questions.

The world speed record for an automobile is 1 028 km/h over a distance of 2.50 km set by a jet-propelled car on the Bonneville Salt Flats in Utah.

Numerical Response

2. If the car starts from rest, the average acceleration over the distance of 2.50 km is _____ m/s^2. (Record your answer to **three** significant digits.)

4. Assuming the car accelerates uniformly, which of the graphs below illustrates the motion of the car?

 A.
 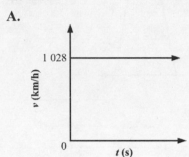

 B.
 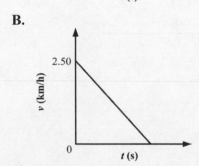

 C.
 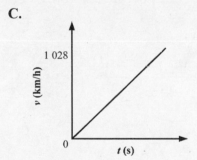

 D.
 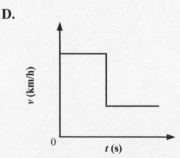

5. A test car on a straight, horizontal track is moving uniformly backward. It begins to slow down and comes to a stop for a period of time. Then it speeds up in the forward direction, reaching a constant velocity for a period of time before decelerating and coming to a stop. The velocity-time graph that illustrates these motions is

A.

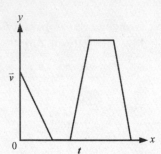

B.

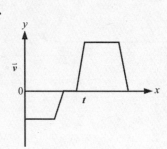

C.

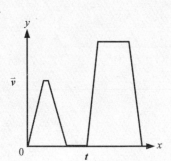

D.

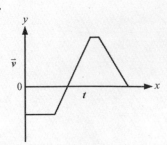

6. Some young children are hunting for treasure at a birthday party. One child walks 11 m east, 21 m north, and 5 m east. Her total displacement has a magnitude of

A. 5 m   B. 22 m

C. 26 m   D. 37 m

Numerical Response

3. A car is driving at 110 km/h 28° E of N. The northward component of the car's velocity is ___ km/h. (Record your answer to **two** significant digits.)

Use the following information to answer the next two questions.

A jet stream is a swiftly flowing air current thousands of kilometres wide and only a few kilometres thick. It exists at the boundary between warm tropical air and cold polar air. The air currents can reach speeds of up to 200 km/h.

7. Keyana is in a plane travelling 800 km/h at 35.0° W of N when the plane encountered the jet stream blowing 200 km/h in a direction 82.0° E of N. What is the resultant speed of the plane?

A. 670 km/h   B. 731 km/h

C. 825 km/h   D. 948 km/h

Numerical Response

4. The resultant direction of the plane would be _____° west of north. (Record your answer to **one** decimal place.)

8. A 2 000 kg car decelerates uniformly from 100 km/h to a complete stop in 10.0 s. The braking force on the car is

A. -2.00×10^2 N

B. -2.00×10^4 N

C. -5.56×10^3 N

D. -7.20×10^4 N

9. A ball is rolled across a table and slowly comes to a stop. According to Newton's laws of motion, the ball stops because

   A. there is a force acting on it

   B. there is no force acting on it

   C. all the forces acting on it are balanced

   D. for every action, there is an equal and opposite reaction

Use the following information to answer the next question.

From each end of a system of two spring scales, a 2.0 kg mass is suspended by cords passing over pulleys, as shown in the diagram.

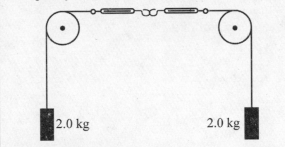

2.0 kg   2.0 kg

Numerical Response

5. The reading on each spring scale is ___ N. (Record your answer to **two** significant digits.)

Use the following diagram to answer the next question.

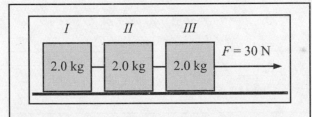

I   II   III

2.0 kg   2.0 kg   2.0 kg   F = 30 N →

10. Three blocks, *I*, *II*, and *III*, are tied together, and each has a mass of 2.0 kg. They are pulled to the right by a 30 N force on a level, frictionless surface. What acceleration does block *II* experience?

   A. 0 m/s²   B. 5.0 m/s²

   C. 7.5 m/s²   D. 15 m/s²

11. A certain force can accelerate a mass at 2.0 m/s². That same force can accelerate a mass three times as big at

   A. 0.50 m/s²

   B. 0.67 m/s²

   C. 5.0 m/s²

   D. 6.0 m/s²

12. A 70.0 kg stunt double on a movie set grabs a handle attached to wire that is attached to a helicopter. The helicopter accelerates upward at 3.50 m/s². The tension on the wire is

   A. 245 N

   B. 442 N

   C. 687 N

   D. 932 N

Numerical Response

6. A 500 g puck slides down a frictionless air table that is inclined at 7.0°. The acceleration of the puck is ___ m/s². (Record your answer to two significant digits.)

Use the following diagram to answer the next question.

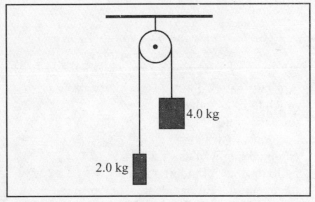

4.0 kg

2.0 kg

13. What will the acceleration of the 4.0 kg mass be when the system is released?

   A. 3.3 m/s² downward

   B. 3.3 m/s² upward

   C. 4.9 m/s² downward

   D. 4.9 m/s² upward

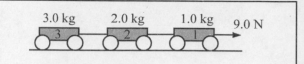

3.0 kg   2.0 kg   1.0 kg   9.0 N

3   2   1

14. If the total force due to friction is 3.0 N, then the wagons in the given diagram are accelerating at

A. 0.50 m/s^2

B. 1.0 m/s^2

C. 2.0 m/s^2

D. 4.0 m/s^2

Numerical Response

7. The net force pulling the third wagon is ___ N. (Record your answer to two significant digits.)

8. Two asteroids in space, one with a mass of 2.0×10^{14} kg and the other with a mass of 3.0×10^{17} kg, experience a gravitational force between them of 4 000 N. The asteroids are $a.b \times 10^c$ m apart. The value of abc is _____. (Record your answer as a **three-digit** number.)

Use the following information to answer the next two questions.

Air bags have done much to reduce the mortality rate of car accidents. Air bags can be thought of as balloons that inflate in the event of a car accident. They provide an air cushion between the occupants in the front of the car and the car's dashboard.

Numerical Response

9. If the driver of a car, with a mass of 60.0 kg, did not have his seat belt fastened when his car collided with a lamp post at 50.0 km/h, the energy of the driver absorbed by the car's airbag, expressed in scientific notation, is $a.bc \times 10^d$ J. The value of *abcd* is _____. (Record your answer as a **four-digit** number.)

15. If the driver is a distance of 0.60 m from the steering wheel, and the driver's side air bag (located in the steering column) has a thickness of 0.30 m when fully inflated, what is the maximum amount of time for the airbag to inflate so that the driver impacts a fully inflated airbag? (Assume the driver moves in uniform motion.)

A. 2.2×10^{-2} s

B. 4.3×10^{-2} s

C. 6.5×10^{-2} s

D. 4.6×10^{1} s

16. A baseball player hits a fly ball that reaches a height of 130 m before it begins to fall back to the field. Given that the mass of the baseball is 150 g, the potential energy of the ball at the top of its flight is

A. 1.91 J   B. 19.1 J

C. 191 J   D. 1.91×10^5 J

Use the following information to answer the next two questions.

A 1 000 kg car travels around a circular curve of radius 80 m with a speed of 72 km/h.

17. What force of friction must be supplied by the road to keep the car from skidding?

A. 2.5×10^2 N

B. 8.4×10^2 N

C. 5.0×10^3 N

D. 6.5×10^4 N

10. The minimum coefficient of friction needed to allow the car to make this turn is _____. (Record your answer to **two** significant digits.)

18. A 60.0 kg pilot in an airplane flies in a vertical loop of radius 950 m. She is upside down at the top of the loop and travelling at 133 m/s. The pilot's apparent weight at this point is

A. 529 N   B. 591 N

C. 1.18 kN   D. 177 kN

Use the following information to answer the next question.

Mercury is the closest planet to the sun and the planet with the second smallest mass in the solar system. It has a mass of 3.28×10^{23} kg and a radius of 2.57×10^6 m.

19. The magnitude of the gravitational field on Mercury ignoring the effects of the sun is

A. 3.31 N/kg   B. 6.67 N/kg

C. 8.51 N/kg   D. 9.81 N/kg

Use your recorded answer from the previous question to answer the following two questions

20. What would a person who weighs 1 000 N on Earth weigh on Mercury?

A. 102 N   B. 302 N

C. 337 N   D. 1 000 N

21. A satellite 275 km above Earth's surface has a period of 1.5 hours. The radius of Earth is 6.37×10^6 m. The orbital speed of this satellite is

A. 3.2×10^2 m/s

B. 7.4×10^3 m/s

C. 7.7×10^3 m/s

D. 2.8×10^7 m/s

22. The force acting on mass **I** at the surface of Earth is 40 N. Mass **II** is three times larger than mass **I**, and it is twice as far from the centre of Earth as mass **I**. How does the net gravitational force on mass **II** compare to the net gravitational force on mass **I**?

A. twice the force

B. the same force

C. half the force

D. three quarters the force

11. An astronomer observing Neptune's moon, Triton, states that it has an average distance from the planet of 3.5×10^5 km and orbits every 5.8 d. If Neptune has a radius of 2.48×10^7 m, the mass of Neptune, expressed in scientific notation, is $a.b \times 10^{cd}$ kg. The value of *abcd* is _____. (Record your answer as a **four-digit** number.)

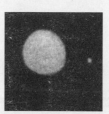

Use the following information to answer the next two questions.

A child's toy consists of a spring with a frog attached to one end and a suction cup attached to the other end. When the compressed spring and the frog are attached to a table top by the suction cup and are then released, the frog "jumps" up and down, repeatedly.

23. Assuming no energy is lost, this type of motion is

A. linear

B. circular

C. transverse

D. simple harmonic

Numerical Response

12. When the toy frog is compressed 3.0 cm, the spring exerts a force of 15 N on the frog. The amount of potential energy stored in the spring is _____ J. (Record your answer to **two** significant digits.)

24. Jim is mowing his lawn. He pushes down on the lawnmower handle with a force of 75 N. The handle is at an angle of 35° with the horizontal. The amount of work Jim does while moving the lawnmower 100 m is

A. 4.3 kJ

B. 5.3 kJ

C. 6.1 kJ

D. 7.5 kJ

Numerical Response

13. A 16.0 kg curling rock travels 24.6 m before stopping. There was a constant force of friction of 2.03 N on the ice surface. The speed at which the rock was released is _____ m/s. (Record your answer to **three** significant digits.)

25. An average adult's heart pumps about 160 mL/beat and beats about seventy times per minute. An approximate energy estimate is 1.0 J/beat. The approximate power output of the heart is

A. 1.7×10^{-2} W

B. 0.86 W

C. 1.2 W

D. 3.1 W

26. A slingshot is used to fire a 600 g rock straight up into the air. The slingshot is pulled back 0.550 m with an average force of 440 N. The rock reaches a height of

A. 21.6 m

B. 41.1 m

C. 202 m

D. 403 m

Use the following information to answer the next question

A 2.00 kg disk slides down a curved ramp from a height of 1.00 m, and then pushes against a spring with a spring constant $k = 500$ N/m, as shown in the diagram.

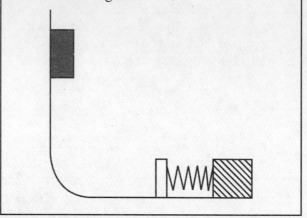

Numerical Response

14. The maximum compression of the spring will be _____ cm. (Record your answer to **three** significant digits.)

27. The relationship between acceleration and period for uniform circular motion is

A. $a_c \propto T$　　　　B. $a_c \propto \dfrac{1}{T}$

C. $a_c \propto T^2$　　　　D. $a_c \propto \dfrac{1}{T^2}$

Use the following information to answer the next question

In 1941, the Tacoma Narrows bridge in Washington State collapsed when winds caused the bridge to oscillate. The standing  wave that formed in the bridge increased in amplitude and eventually caused the bridge to collapse.

28. This is an example of

   A. harmonics

   B. the Doppler Effect

   C. mechanical resonance

   D. the interference of waves

29. The clap of thunder often heard from nearby lightning strikes can be short lived but very loud. This sound can best be described as a

   A. transverse pulse with a large amplitude

   B. transverse pulse with a small amplitude

   C. longitudinal pulse with a large amplitude

   D. longitudinal pulse with a small amplitude

30. What is the relationship between the temperature of air and the speed of sound in air?

   A. As the temperature increases, the speed of sound increases.

   B. As the temperature increases, the speed of sound decreases.

   C. The speed of sound is at its slowest when air temperature is 0°C.

   D. The speed of sound will remain constant at different air temperatures.

Use the following graph to answer the next question.

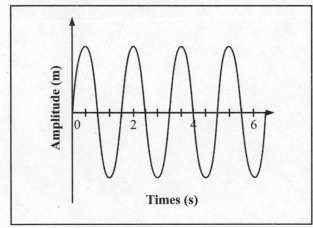

31. The period of this wave is approximately

   A. 0.8 s   **B.** 1.6 s

   C. 2.4 s   **D.** 3.2 s

32. A sound wave from a tuning fork has a frequency of 508 Hz. Its wavelength is measured to be 67.5 cm. The speed of sound is

   A. 7.60 m/s   **B.** 34.3 m/s

   C. 343 m/s   **D.** 760 m/s

Use the following diagram to answer the next question.

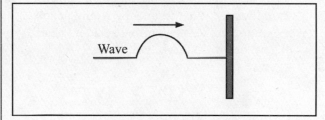

33. What will the above wave look like after it has reflected from the wall?

   A.

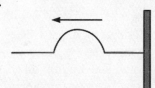

   B.

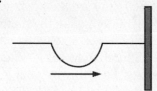

   C.

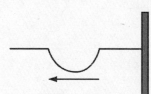

   D.

34. Many people suffer from tinnitus, a constant ringing in the ears. There is no known cure for this. One possible treatment to temporarily eliminate this constant noise is to use a headset or earplugs to send certain frequencies of sound into the person's ears. This treatment is based on the wave property of

A. reflection

B. refraction

C. diffraction

D. interference

35. An ambulance pulls away from an accident scene at 35.0 m/s. Its siren emits a 600 Hz sound wave. What frequency would people remaining at the scene of the accident hear? (The speed of sound is 343 m/s.)

A. 285 Hz

B. 355 Hz

C. 544 Hz

D. 674 Hz

Written Response

1. A 70 kg football player kicks a 1.0 kg football at an initial velocity of 20 m/s, 60° to the horizon. The 3.0 m high crossbar of the goal is 30 m away from where the ball is kicked. Assuming the player kicks the football directly toward the goal, and assuming that gravity and the football player are the only forces that act on the football, will the football travel far enough to go over the crossbar? Justify your answer with appropriate calculations of horizontal and vertical distances.

2. A Light Rail Transit train stops at two stations that are 2.5 km apart. From the first station, the train accelerates from rest at 2.5 m/s^2 until it reaches a cruising speed of 15 m/s. It then travels at this speed for 2 minutes and 40 seconds. Then, the train slows to a stop. With what rate of deceleration does the Light Rail Transit train slow down?

ANSWERS AND SOLUTIONS—PRACTICE TEST 2

1. C	NR5. 20	NR10. 0.51	NR14. 28.0
NR1. 58	10. B	18. A	27. D
2. D	11. B	19. A	28. C
3. C	12. D	20. C	29. C
NR2. 16.3	NR6. 1.2	21. C	30. A
4. C	13. A	22. D	31. B
5. B	14. B	NR11. 1226	32. C
6. C	NR7. 3.0	23. D	33. C
NR3. 97	NR8. 109	NR12. 0.23	34. D
7. B	NR9. 5793	24. C	35. C
NR4. 20.9	15. A	NR13. 2.50	WR1. See Solution
8. C	16. C	25. C	WR2. See Solution
9. A	17. C	26. B	

1. C

Scalars have no direction. Examples of scalars are time, mass, speed, and distance.

Vectors have direction. Examples are force, velocity, and displacement.

NR 1   58

$$\vec{v}_{average} = \frac{\vec{d}}{t}$$
$$= \frac{807 \text{ m}}{14 \text{ s}}$$
$$= 58 \text{ m/s}$$

2. D

The water is in free fall, so it undergoes uniform acceleration, increasing its velocity.

3. C

$$E_m = E_k + E_p$$
$$= \frac{1}{2}mv^2 + mgh$$
$$= \frac{1}{2}(10 \text{ kg})(4.0 \text{ m/s})^2 + (10 \text{ kg})(9.81 \text{ m/s}^2)(807 \text{ m})$$
$$= 80 \text{ J} + 79 \text{ }167 \text{ J}$$
$$= 79 \text{ kJ}$$

NR 2   16.3

$$v_i = 0$$
$$v_f = 1 \text{ }028 \frac{\text{km}}{\text{h}} \times \frac{1 \text{ }000 \text{ m}}{\text{km}} \times \frac{1 \text{ h}}{3 \text{ }600 \text{ s}}$$
$$= 285.6 \text{ m/s}$$
$$d = 2.50 \times 10^3 \text{ m}$$
$$v_f^2 = v_i^2 + 2ad$$
$$a = \frac{v_f^2 - v_i^2}{2d}$$
$$= \frac{(285.6 \text{ m/s})^2 - (0 \text{ m/s})^2}{2(2.5 \times 10^3 \text{ m})}$$
$$= 16.3 \text{ m/s}^2$$

Note: It is helpful for problem solving to identify what is given and then choose the correct formula.

4. C

Since the car begins from rest, its velocity should be 0 km/h at $t = 0$ s. As you are assuming that the car accelerates uniformly, its velocity increases linearly over time.

5. B

Moving backward would be a negative velocity. Therefore, choices **A** and **C** are eliminated. Choice **B** is correct because it includes a period when the car is stopped $(\vec{v} = 0)$ before it moves with forward (+) velocity.

6. C

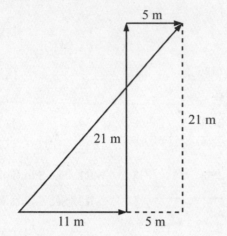

Magnitude of displacement is

$d = \sqrt{(16 \text{ m})^2 + (21 \text{ m})^2}$
$\quad = 26 \text{ m}$

NR 3   97

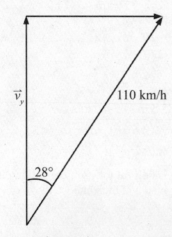

$\vec{v}_y = 110 \text{ km/h} (\cos 28°)$
$\quad = 97 \text{ km/h north}$

7. B

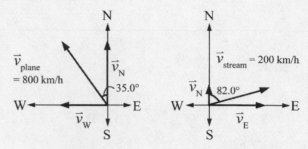

Considering north and west direction as positive, components for the plane's velocity

$v_N = (800 \text{ km/h}) \cos 35.0°$
$\quad = 655.3 \text{ km/h}$
$\therefore \vec{v}_N = 655.3 \text{ km/h north}$
$v_W = (800 \text{ km/h}) \sin 35.0°$
$\quad = 458.9 \text{ km/h}$
$\therefore \vec{v}_W = 458.9 \text{ km/h west}$

Components for the jet stream

$v_N = (200 \text{ km/h}) \cos 82.0°$
$\quad = 27.83 \text{ km/h}$
$\therefore \vec{v}_N = 27.83 \text{ km/h north}$
$v_E = (200 \text{ km/h}) \sin 82.0°$
$\quad = 198.1 \text{ km/h}$
$\therefore \vec{v}_E = 198.1 \text{ km/h east}$
$\quad = -198.1 \text{ km/h west}$

Resultant components

$\vec{v}_N = (655.3 \text{ km/h}) + (27.83 \text{ km/h})$
$\quad = 683 \text{ km/h}$
$\vec{v}_W = (458.9 \text{ km/h}) + (-198.1 \text{ km/h})$
$\quad = 260.8 \text{ km/h}$

To find the magnitude of the resultant velocity use Pythagoras' theorem.

$v_R^2 = (683.1 \text{ km/h})^2 + (260.8 \text{ km/h})^2$
$v_R = 731 \text{ km/h}$

NR 4   20.9

$\theta = \tan^{-1} \left(\dfrac{260.8 \text{ km/h}}{683.1 \text{ km/h}} \right)$
$\quad = 20.9° \text{ W of N}$

8. C

$$\vec{v}_i = 100\frac{km}{h} \times \frac{1\ 000\ km}{1\ km} \times \frac{1\ h}{3\ 600\ s}$$
$$= 27.8\ m/s$$
$$\vec{a} = \frac{\Delta\vec{v}}{t}$$
$$= \frac{0 - 27.8\ m/s}{10.0\ s}$$
$$= -2.78\ m/s$$
$$\vec{F}_{braking} = m\vec{a}$$
$$= (2\ 000\ kg)(-2.78\ m/s^2)$$
$$= -5.56 \times 10^3\ N$$

9. A

The friction force opposes the motion giving it a negative acceleration. Therefore, it slows down and obeys $\vec{F}_{net} = m\vec{a}$, i.e., an object will accelerate in the direction of the net force acting on it (Newton's second law).

NR 5   20

$$F = mg$$
$$= (2.0\ kg)(9.81\ m/s^2)$$
$$= 20\ N$$

Each scale has 20 N acting on it.

10. B

$$\vec{F}_{net} = m\vec{a}$$
$$\vec{a} = \frac{\vec{F}_{net}}{m}$$
$$= \frac{\vec{F}_{net}}{m_a + m_b + m_c}$$
$$= \frac{30\ N}{(2.0\ kg + 2.0\ kg + 2.0\ kg)}$$
$$\vec{a} = 5.0\ m/s^2\ forward$$

Note: As the blocks are tied together, they act as one mass. Acceleration is in the direction of the applied force. There is no friction, so 30 N is the net force. The force of gravity is not used because the objects are not moving up or down (i.e., vertically).

11. B

$$\vec{a} = \frac{\vec{F}}{m}$$
$$\frac{\vec{a}_{new}}{\vec{a}_{old}} = \frac{\frac{\vec{F}}{3m}}{\frac{\vec{F}}{m}}$$
$$= \frac{1}{3}$$
$$\vec{a}_{new} = \frac{1}{3}(2.0\ m/s^2)$$
$$= 0.67\ m/s^2\ forward$$

12. D

$$\vec{F}_{net} = m\vec{a}$$
$$\vec{F}_{net} = \vec{F}_T + m\vec{g}$$
$$m\vec{a} = \vec{F}_T + m\vec{g}$$
$$\vec{F}_T = m\vec{a} - m\vec{g}$$
$$= 70.0\ kg(3.50\ m/s^2) - 70.0\ kg(-9.81\ m/s^2)$$
$$= 932\ N\ upward$$

NR 6   1.2

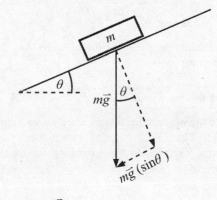

$$\vec{F}_{net} = m\vec{a} = \vec{F}_{\parallel}$$
$$ma = mg\sin\theta$$
$$a = g\sin\theta$$
$$= (9.81\ m/s^2)(\sin 7.0°)$$
$$= 1.2\ m/s^2$$
$$\therefore \vec{a} = 1.2\ m/s^2\ down\ the\ ramp$$

13. A

$$\vec{F}_{net} = \vec{F}_{g4} - \vec{F}_{g2}$$
$$m_T\vec{a} = m_4\vec{g} - m_2\vec{g}$$
$$(4.0\text{ kg} + 2.0\text{ kg})\vec{a} = (4.0\text{ kg})(-9.81\text{ N/kg})$$
$$- (2.0\text{ kg})(-9.81\text{ N/kg})$$
$$\vec{a} = \frac{(4.0\text{ kg})(-9.81\text{ N/kg}) - (2.0\text{ kg})(-9.81\text{ N/kg})}{6.0\text{ kg}}$$
$$\vec{a} = \frac{-19.6\text{ N}}{6.0\text{ kg}}$$
$$\vec{a} = -3.3\text{ m/s}^2, \text{ or } 3.3\text{ m/s}^2 \text{ downward}$$

14. B

$$\vec{F}_{net} = \vec{F}_{app} + \vec{F}_{f}$$
$$\vec{F}_{net} = (9.0\text{ N}) + (-3.0\text{ N})$$
$$= 6.0\text{ N}$$
$$m_{total} = 3.0\text{ kg} + 2.0\text{ kg} + 1.0\text{ kg}$$
$$= 6.0\text{ kg}$$
$$\vec{F}_{net} = m\vec{a}$$
$$\vec{a} = \frac{\vec{F}_{net}}{m}$$
$$= \frac{6.0\text{ N}}{6.0\text{ kg}}$$
$$= 1.0\text{ m/s}^2$$

Acceleration is along the direction of the applied force.

NR 7   3.0

Since the objects are linked, they move as one object. Therefore, the third wagon accelerates at 1.0 m/s^2 like the rest. The net force on the third wagon is

$$\vec{F}_{net} = m\vec{a}$$
$$= 3.0\text{ kg} (1.0\text{ m/s}^2)$$
$$= 3.0\text{ N}$$

NR 8   109

The magnitude of the gravitational force is

$$F_g = \frac{Gm_1m_2}{r^2}$$
$$r = \sqrt{\frac{Gm_1m_2}{F_g}}$$
$$= \sqrt{\frac{\left(6.67\times10^{-11}\frac{\text{N}\cdot\text{m}^2}{\text{kg}^2}\right)(2.0\times10^{14}\text{kg})(3.0\times10^{17}\text{kg})}{4\,000\text{ N}}}$$
$$= 1.0\times10^9\text{ m}$$

NR 9   5793

$$\text{speed } v = 50.0\frac{\text{km}}{\text{h}} \times \frac{1\,000\text{ m}}{1\text{ km}} \times \frac{1\text{ h}}{3\,600\text{ s}}$$
$$= 13.89\text{ m/s}$$
$$E_k = \frac{1}{2}mv^2$$
$$= \frac{1}{2}(60.0\text{ kg})(13.89\text{ m/s})^2$$
$$= 5.79\times10^3\text{ J}$$

15. A

$$\text{speed } v = 50.0\frac{\text{km}}{\text{h}} \times \frac{1\,000\text{ m}}{1\text{ km}} \times \frac{1\text{ h}}{3\,600\text{ s}}$$
$$= 13.89\text{ m/s}$$
$$t = \frac{\Delta d}{v}$$
$$= \frac{(0.60\text{ m} - 0.30\text{ m})}{13.89\text{ m/s}}$$
$$= 0.022\text{ s}$$
$$= 2.2\times10^{-2}\text{ s}$$

16. C

$$E_p = mgh$$
$$= (0.150\text{ kg})(9.81\text{ N/kg})(130\text{ m})$$
$$= 191\text{ J}$$

17. C

$$\text{speed } v = 72\frac{\text{km}}{\text{h}} \times \frac{1\,000}{1\text{ km}} \times \frac{1\text{ h}}{3\,600\text{ s}}$$
$$= 20\text{ m/s}$$

The magnitude of the net force $\vec{F}_c$ must equal the force of friction.

$$F_c = \frac{mv^2}{r}$$
$$= \frac{(1\,000\text{ kg})(20\text{ m/s})^2}{80\text{ m}}$$
$$= 5.0\times10^3\text{ N}$$

NR 10   0.51

The coefficient of friction (μ) is found by dividing the force of friction required to produce sliding $(\vec{F}_f)$ by the normal force between the surfaces $(\vec{F}_N)$.

The magnitude of the normal force

$$F_N = mg$$
$$= (1\,000 \text{ kg})(9.81 \text{ m/s}^2)$$
$$= 9.81 \times 10^3 \text{ N}$$

$$\mu = \frac{F_f}{F_N}$$
$$= \frac{5.0 \times 10^3 \text{ N}}{9.81 \times 10^3 \text{ N}}$$
$$= 0.51$$

18. A

The apparent weight is the normal force, so:

$$\vec{F}_{net} = \vec{F}_N + \vec{F}_g$$
$$\vec{F}_{net} = \vec{F}_c$$

considering magnitude only

$$ma_c = F_N + mg$$

$$F_N = \frac{mv^2}{r} - mg$$

$$= \frac{(60.0 \text{ kg})(133 \text{ m/s})^2}{950 \text{ m}} - 60.0 \text{ kg}(9.81 \text{ m/s}^2)$$

$$= 529 \text{ N}$$

19. A

$$g_M = \frac{Gm_M}{r^2}$$

$$g_M = \left(6.67 \times 10^{-11} \frac{\text{N} \cdot \text{m}}{\text{kg}^2}\right) \frac{(3.28 \times 10^{23} \text{ kg})}{(2.57 \times 10^6 \text{ m})^2}$$

$$g_M = 3.31 \text{ N/kg}$$

Note: This is roughly one-third that of Earth's field (9.81 N/kg).

20. C

$$\vec{F}_g = mg \text{ [on Earth]}$$
$$1\,000 \text{ N} = m(9.81 \text{ N/kg})$$
$$m = \frac{1\,000 \text{ N}}{9.81 \text{ N/kg}}$$
$$= 101.9 \text{ kg}$$

Note: This is the person's mass, which is constant.

$$\vec{F}_g = m\vec{g}_M \text{ [on Mercury]}$$
$$\vec{F}_g = (101.9 \text{ kg})(3.31 \text{ N/kg})$$
$$= 337 \text{ N}$$

21. C

$$\vec{d}_{\text{to surface}} = 275 \text{ km} \times \frac{1\,000 \text{ m}}{1 \text{ km}}$$
$$= 2.75 \times 10^5 \text{ m}$$

$$T = 1.5 \text{ h} \times \frac{3\,600 \text{ s}}{1 \text{ h}}$$
$$= 5.4 \times 10^3 \text{ s}$$

Calculate the average speed.

$$v = \frac{d}{t}$$
$$= \frac{2\pi r}{T}$$
$$= \frac{2\pi (6.37 \times 10^6 \text{ m} + 2.75 \times 10^5 \text{ m})}{5.4 \times 10^3 \text{ s}}$$
$$= 7.7 \times 10^3 \text{ m/s}$$

Note: Earth's radius is added to the distance above Earth's surface to find the total orbital radius to Earth's centre.

22. D

$$F_g = \frac{Gm_1 m_2}{r^2}$$

Mass **II** is 3 times larger than mass **I**, so the effect of its mass would make the net gravitational force three times larger because $F \propto m$. The distance between mass **II** and Earth's centre, however, is twice as great.

The force of gravity is weakened by the increased distance by 2^2, or 4 times since $F \propto \frac{1}{r^2}$.

Therefore, the total effect of the differences in mass and distance on the net gravitational force of mass **II** is $\frac{3}{4}$ times the net gravitational force of mass **I**.

NR 11   1226

$$d_{\text{to surface}} = 3.5 \times 10^5 \text{ km} \times \frac{1\,000 \text{ km}}{1 \text{ km}}$$
$$= 3.5 \times 10^8 \text{ m}$$

$$T = 5.8 \text{ d} \times \frac{24 \text{ h}}{1 \text{ d}} \times \frac{3\,600 \text{ s}}{1 \text{ h}}$$
$$= 5.01 \times 10^5 \text{ s}$$

$$\vec{F}_{\text{c}} = \vec{F}_{\text{g}}$$
$$\frac{4\pi^2 m_{\text{T}} r}{T^2} = \frac{G m_{\text{T}} m_{\text{N}}}{r^2}$$
$$m_{\text{N}} = \frac{4\pi^2 r^3}{G T^2}$$
$$= \frac{4\pi^2 \left(3.5 \times 10^8 \text{ m} + 2.48 \times 10^7 \text{ m}\right)^3}{6.67 \times 10^{-11} \dfrac{\text{N} \cdot \text{m}^2}{\text{kg}^2} \left(5.01 \times 10^5 \text{ s}\right)^2}$$
$$= 1.2 \times 10^{26} \text{ kg}$$

23. D

The oscillation of the frog (assuming no energy is lost) repeats periodically as simple harmonic motion.

NR 12   0.23

The magnitude of the compression force is
$$F_{\text{net}} = kx$$
$$k = \frac{F_{\text{net}}}{x}$$
$$k = \frac{15 \text{ N}}{0.030 \text{ m}}$$
$$= 5.0 \times 10^2 \text{ N/m}$$
$$E_{\text{p}} = \frac{1}{2} kx$$
$$= \frac{1}{2} \left(500 \text{ N/m}\right)\left(0.030 \text{ m}\right)^2$$
$$= 0.23 \text{ J}$$

24. C

$$W = Fd \cos\theta$$
$$= \left(75 \text{ N}\right)\left(100 \text{ m}\right)\cos 35°$$
$$= 6.1 \text{ kJ}$$

NR 13   2.50

Do not forget that the force of friction is in the opposite direction of the displacement of the curling rock and is, therefore, negative.

$$W = Fd$$
$$W = \Delta E = E_{\text{f}} - E_{\text{i}}$$
$$Fd = 0 - \frac{1}{2} mv^2$$
$$v = \sqrt{\frac{-2Fd}{m}}$$
$$= \sqrt{\frac{-2\left(-2.03 \text{ N}\right)\left(24.6 \text{ m}\right)}{16.0 \text{ kg}}}$$
$$= 2.50 \text{ m/s}$$

25. C

This is a unit analysis question. You want to find J/s or Watts.

$$\frac{1.0 \text{ J}}{1 \text{ beat}} \times \frac{70 \text{ beats}}{60 \text{ s}} = 1.2 \text{ J/s}$$
$$= 1.2 \text{ W}$$

26. B

The work done stretching the slingshot is found with
$$W = Fd$$
$$= 440 \text{ N} \times 0.550 \text{ m}$$
$$= 242 \text{ J}$$

This is the amount of kinetic energy that the slingshot gives to the rock and is also the amount of potential energy the rock has at its highest point.

Therefore: $E_{\text{p}} = mgh$
$$h = \frac{E_{\text{p}}}{mg}$$
$$= \frac{242 \text{ J}}{\left(0.600 \text{ kg}\right)\left(9.81 \text{ m/s}^2\right)}$$
$$= 41.1 \text{ m}$$

NR 14 28.0

$$\Sigma E_i = \Sigma E_f$$
$$mgh = \frac{1}{2}kx^2$$
$$x = \sqrt{\frac{2mgh}{k}}$$
$$= \sqrt{\frac{2(2.00\text{ kg})(9.81\text{ m/s}^2)(1.00\text{ m})}{500\text{ N/m}}}$$
$$= 28.0\text{ cm}$$

27. D

In circular motion, $a_c = \dfrac{v^2}{r}$ and $v = \dfrac{2\pi r}{T}$

$$\therefore a_c = \frac{\left(\dfrac{2\pi r}{T}\right)^2}{r}$$

(cross multiply and square the speed formula)

$$a_c \not{r} = \frac{4\pi^2 r^{\not{2}}}{T^2}$$

(an r will cancel)

$$a_c = \frac{4\pi^2 r}{T^2} \therefore a_c \propto \frac{1}{T^2}$$

It is an inverse square relationship.

28. C

A standing wave formed in the bridge as the wind velocity was sufficient to create nodes and anti-nodes.

The maximum amplitude (resonance) caused the bridge to fall apart.

29. C

All sound waves are longitudinal. A large amplitude signifies a very large molecular disturbance of the air, which is responsible for creating the loud sound we hear.

30. A

Sound travels more slowly in air that is more dense. Air at a lower temperature is more dense than air at a higher temperature. This means that as air temperature increases, the speed of sound will also increase. This is a direct relationship, and it applies even at sub zero temperatures.

31. B

The period is the time for one complete vibration that occurs at 1.6 seconds on the time scale.

32. C

$$v = \lambda f$$
$$= 0.675\text{ m} \times 508\text{ Hz}$$
$$= 343\text{ m/s}$$

33. C

Assuming an elastic collision, no energy is lost. So the amplitude is constant but is inverted, as the wall is a fixed-end reflection.

34. D

When the two frequencies overlap, destructive interference occurs and eliminates the waves (nodes).

35. C

The ambulance is moving away. Therefore, the observed frequency will be lower than the emitted frequency.

Therefore

$$f' = f\left(\frac{v}{v + v_s}\right)$$
$$= (600\text{ Hz})\left(\frac{343\text{ m/s}}{343\text{ m/s} + 35.0\text{ m/s}}\right)$$
$$= 544\text{ Hz}$$

1. *Assuming the player kicks the football directly toward the goal, and assuming that gravity and the football player are the only forces that act on the football, will the football travel far enough to go over the crossbar? Justify your answer with appropriate calculations of horizontal and vertical distances.*

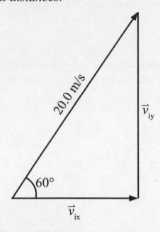

$v_{ix} = (20 \text{ m/s})\cos 60°$
$\quad = 10 \text{ m/s}$
$v_{iy} = (20 \text{ m/s})\sin 60°$
$\quad = 17.3 \text{ m/s}$

If the football player and gravity are the only forces acting upon the football, then the initial horizontal component represents a uniform motion. The ball will move 10.0 m/s horizontally as a constant. Solve for the time it takes the ball to get to the goal. The horizontal distance is

$d = v_{ix}t$
$30 \text{ m} = 10 \text{ m/s} \times t$
$t = \dfrac{30 \text{ m}}{10 \text{ m/s}}$
$t = 3.0 \text{ s}$

Now find the height (vertical displacement) of the ball after 3.0 seconds of flight.

$\vec{d}_y = \vec{v}_{iy}t + \dfrac{1}{2}\vec{g}t^2$

$\quad = 17.3 \text{ m/s} \times 3.0 \text{ s} + \dfrac{1}{2}\left(-9.81 \text{ m/s}^2\right)(3.0 \text{ s})^2$

$\quad = 51.9 \text{ m} - 44.1 \text{ m}$
$\quad = 7.8 \text{ m}$

When the ball has travelled 30 m toward the goal, it will be 7.8 metres above the ground, which easily clears the 3.0-m high crossbar.

2. *With what rate of deceleration does the Light Rail Transit train slow down?*

First, find out how far the Light Rail Transit train goes while speeding up.

$v_f^2 = v_i^2 + 2ad$

$d = \dfrac{v_f^2 - v_i^2}{2a}$

$\quad = \dfrac{(15 \text{ m/s})^2 - 0}{2(2.5 \text{ m/s}^2)}$

$\quad = 45.0 \text{ m}$

Next, find out how far the Light Rail Transit train travels at its constant speed.

$d = vt$
$\quad = 15 \text{ m/s} \times 160 \text{ s}$
$\quad = 2\,400 \text{ m}$

Then, find the distance the train uses to slow down and stop.

$d_{stop} = 2\,500 \text{ m} - (2\,400 \text{ m} + 45 \text{ m})$
$\quad = 55 \text{ m}$

Finally, calculate the rate of deceleration.

$a = \dfrac{v_f^2 - v_i^2}{2d}$

$\quad = \dfrac{0 - (15 \text{ m/s})^2}{2(55 \text{ m})}$

$\quad = -2.0 \text{ m/s}^2$

The Light Rail Transit train slows down at a rate of 2.0 m/s^2.

Students are awarded stars for each lesson they review or every assessment they complete. As students accumulate stars, they can use them to purchase rewards to build a personalized avatar. This provides incentive by providing a fun, interactive, motivational reward for participation and success.

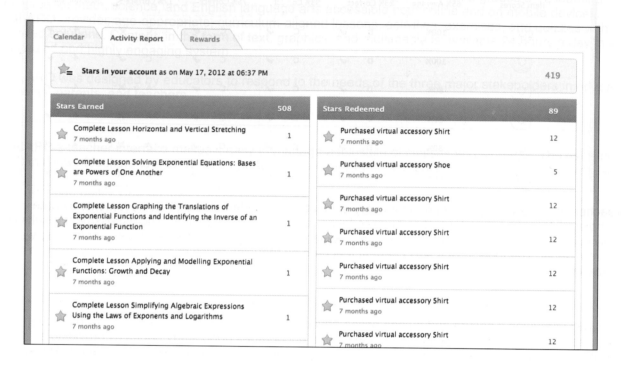

All progress is saved instantly so students can access pick up their mobile devices and continue where they left off on their home computers.

The **SOLARO** parent interface allows parents to monitor the individual progress for each of their children, and it provides detailed reports for each child's account. These easy to read reports show how many activities have been completed, when they were reported, the progress of the student through their courses, the level of achievement on tests and assignments, and deficiencies that may need to be addressed. Parents can configure reports to automatically send to their mobile devices.

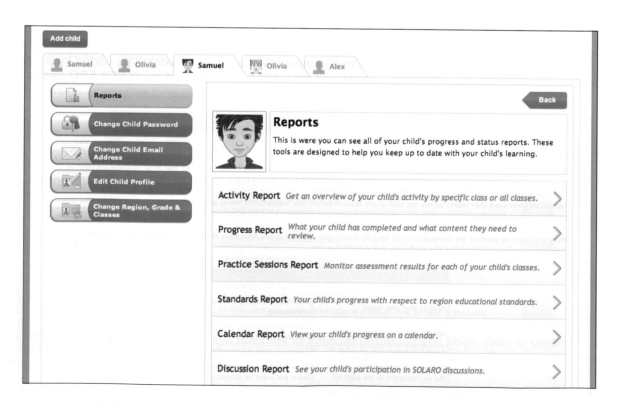

Appendices

PHYSICS DATA TABLES

KINEMATICS

$$\vec{v} = \frac{\vec{d}}{t}$$

$$\vec{a} = \frac{\vec{v}_f - \vec{v}_i}{t}$$

$$\vec{d} = \vec{v}_i t + \frac{1}{2}\vec{a}t^2$$

$$\vec{d} = \left(\frac{\vec{v}_f + \vec{v}_i}{2}\right)t$$

$$v_f^2 = v_i^2 + 2ad$$

$$\vec{F} = m\vec{a}$$

$$W = Fd$$

$$W = Fd\cos\theta$$

$$E_k = \frac{1}{2}mv^2$$

$$E_p = mgh \,(\text{gravitational})$$

$$P = \frac{W}{t} \ \text{ or } \ \frac{\Delta E}{t}$$

MOMENTUM AND IMPULSE

$$\vec{p} = m\vec{v}$$

$$\vec{F}t = m\Delta\vec{v}$$

FORCES AND FIELDS

$$\vec{F}_g = m\vec{g}$$

$$F_c = \frac{mv^2}{r}$$

$$F_g = \frac{Gm_1 m_2}{r^2}$$

$$g = \frac{Gm}{r^2}$$

$$B = \frac{\mu_0 I}{2\pi r}$$

$$\vec{B} = \mu_0 In$$

$$\frac{\vec{F}}{l} = \frac{\mu_0 I_1 I_2}{2\pi r}$$

$$\vec{E} = \frac{\vec{F}_e}{q}$$

$$\vec{F} = -k\vec{x}$$

$$E_p = \frac{1}{2}kx^2$$

$$F_e = \frac{kq_1 q_2}{r^2}$$

$$E = \frac{kq}{r^2}$$

$$V = \frac{kq}{r}$$

$$F_m = B_\perp Il$$

$$F_m = qvB_\perp$$

$$V = \frac{\Delta E}{q}$$

$$W = qEd$$

ELECTROMAGNETIC RADIATION

$$c = \lambda f$$

$$f = \frac{1}{T}$$

$$\frac{\sin \theta_1}{\sin \theta_2} = \frac{v_1}{v_2} = \frac{\lambda_1}{\lambda_2} = \frac{n_2}{n_1}$$

$$\lambda = \frac{dx}{nl}$$

$$\lambda = \frac{d \sin \theta}{n}$$

$$\sin \theta = \frac{m\lambda}{w} \text{ (for a min)}$$

$$\sin \theta = \frac{\left(m + \frac{1}{2}\right)\lambda}{w} \text{ (for a max)}$$

$$\frac{1}{f} = \frac{1}{d_o} + \frac{1}{d_i}$$

$$E = hf$$

$$E = \frac{hc}{\lambda}$$

$$E_{k\,max} = hf - W$$

$$W = hf_0$$

$$E_{k\,max} = qV_{stop}$$

$$p = \frac{h}{\lambda} = \frac{hf}{c}$$

$$M = \frac{h_i}{h_0} = -\frac{d_i}{d_0}$$

ATOMIC PHYSICS

$$E = mc^2$$

$$E = hf$$

$$E = \frac{hc}{\lambda}$$

$$E_{k\,max} = hf - W$$

$$W = hf_0$$

$$E_{k\,max} = qV_{stop}$$

$$n\lambda = 2\pi r_n$$

$$E_n = \frac{E_1}{n^2}$$

$$\frac{1}{\lambda} = R_H \left(\frac{1}{n_1^2} - \frac{1}{n_u^2} \right)$$

$$r_n = r_1 n^2$$

$$\lambda = \frac{h}{m\bar{v}}$$

$$\bar{p} = h\lambda = \frac{hf}{c}$$

$$N = N_0 \left(\frac{1}{2} \right)^n$$

SPECIAL RELATIVITY

$$\gamma = \frac{1}{\sqrt{1 - \frac{v^2}{c^2}}}$$

$$\Delta t' = \gamma \Delta t = \frac{\Delta t}{\sqrt{1 - \frac{v^2}{c^2}}}$$

$$L' = \frac{L_0}{\gamma} = \left(\sqrt{1 - \frac{v^2}{c^2}} \right) L_0$$

CONSTANTS

Acceleration due to gravity near Earth	$g = 9.81 \ \text{m/s}^2$
Gravitational field near Earth	$g = 9.81 \ \text{N/kg}$
Gravitational constant	$G = 6.67 \times 10^{-11} \ \text{N} \cdot \text{m}^2/\text{kg}^2$
Index of refraction (air)	$n = 1.00$
Speed of light (air or vacuum)	$c = 3.00 \times 10^8 \ \text{m/s}$
Coulomb's constant	$k = 8.99 \times 10^9 \ \text{N} \cdot \text{m}^2/\text{C}^2$
Permeability of free space	$\mu_0 = 4\pi \times 10^{-7} \ \text{T} \cdot \text{m/A}$
Elementary charge	$e = 1.60 \times 10^{-19} \ \text{C}$
Electron volt	$1 \ \text{eV} = 1.60 \times 10^{-19} \ \text{J}$

Hydrogen atom (Bohr model)

1st orbit radius	$r_1 = 5.29 \times 10^{-11} \ \text{m}$
1st orbit energy	$E_1 = 2.18 \times 10^{-18} \ \text{J} \ (13.6 \ \text{eV})$
Planck's constant	$h = 6.63 \times 10^{-34} \ \text{J} \cdot \text{s}$
Rydberg's constant for hydrogen	$R_H = 1.10 \times 10^7 \ \text{m}^{-1}$

Particles	Rest Mass	Charge
alpha particle	6.65×10^{-27} kg	3.20×10^{-19} C
electron	9.11×10^{-31} kg	-1.60×10^{-19} C
neutron	1.67×10^{-27} kg	0
proton	1.67×10^{-27} kg	1.60×10^{-19} C

PREFIXES

Name	Symbol	Multiplier	Name	Symbol	Multiplier
yotta-	Y	10^{24}	deci-	d	10^{-1}
terra-	T	10^{12}	centi-	c	10^{-2}
giga-	G	10^{9}	milli-	m	10^{-3}
mega-	M	10^{6}	micro-	μ	10^{-6}
kilo-	k	10^{3}	nano-	n	10^{-9}
hecto-	h	10^{2}	pico-	p	10^{-12}
deca-	da	10^{1}	femto-	f	10^{-15}

Periodic Table of the Elements

LEGEND

METALS

NON-METALS

METALLOIDS

KEY

Atomic Number → 28
Symbol of Element → **Ni**
Atomic Mass → 58.71

1 **H** 1.01																	2 **He** 4.00
3 **Li** 6.94	4 **Be** 9.01											5 **B** 10.81	6 **C** 12.01	7 **N** 14.01	8 **O** 16.00	9 **F** 19.00	10 **NE** 20.17
11 **Na** 22.99	12 **Mg** 24.31											13 **Al** 26.98	14 **Si** 28.09	15 **P** 30.97	16 **S** 32.06	17 **Cl** 35.45	18 **Ar** 39.95
19 **K** 39.10	20 **Ca** 40.08	21 **Sc** 44.96	22 **Ti** 47.90	23 **V** 50.94	24 **Cr** 52.00	25 **Mn** 54.94	26 **Fe** 55.85	27 **Co** 58.93	28 **Ni** 58.71	29 **Cu** 63.55	30 **Zn** 65.38	31 **Ga** 69.72	32 **Ge** 72.59	33 **As** 74.92	34 **Se** 78.96	35 **Br** 79.90	36 **Kr** 83.80
37 **Rb** 85.47	38 **Sr** 87.62	39 **Y** 88.91	40 **Zr** 91.22	41 **Nb** 92.91	42 **Mo** 95.94	43 **Tc** 98.91	44 **Ru** 101.07	45 **Rh** 102.91	46 **Pd** 106.40	47 **Ag** 107.87	48 **Cd** 112.41	49 **In** 114.82	50 **Sn** 118.69	51 **Sb** 121.75	52 **Te** 127	53 **I** 126.90	54 **Xe** 131.30
55 **Cs** 132.91	56 **Ba** 137.33	57 **La** 138.91	72 **Hf** 178.49	73 **Ta** 180.95	74 **W** 183.85	75 **Re** 186.21	76 **Os** 190.20	77 **Ir** 192.22	78 **Pt** 195.09	79 **Au** 196.97	80 **Hg** 200.59	81 **Tl** 204.37	82 **Pb** 207.19	83 **Bi** 208.98	84 **Po** (209)	85 **At** (210)	86 **Rn** (222)
87 **Fr** (223)	88 **Ra** 226.03	89 **Ac** (227)	104 Rf (266)	105 Db (262)	106 Sg (263)	107 Bh (262)	108 Hs (265)	109 Mt (266)	110 Ds (269)	111 Rg (280)							

58 **Ce** 140.12	59 **Pr** 140.91	60 **Nd** 144.24	61 Pm (145)	62 **Sm** 150.35	63 **Eu** 151.96	64 **Gd** 157.25	65 **Tb** 158.93	66 **Dy** 162.50	67 **Ho** 164.93	68 **Er** 167.26	69 **Tm** 168.93	70 **Yb** 173.04	71 **Lu** 174.97
90 **Th** 232.04	91 **Pa** 231.04	92 **U** 238.03	93 Np 237.05	94 Pu (244)	95 Am (243)	96 Cm (247)	97 Bk (247)	98 Cf (242)	99 Es (252)	100 Fm (257)	101 Md (258)	102 No (259)	103 Lr (260)

CREDITS

Every effort has been made to provide proper acknowledgement of the original source and to comply with copyright law. However, some attempts to establish original copyright ownership may have been unsuccessful. If copyright ownership can be identified, please notify Castle Rock Research Corp so that appropriate corrective action can be taken.

Some of the questions in the Practice Exams were taken from the Alberta Diploma Examinations with permission from Alberta Education.

IMAGES

Some images used in this publication are copyright *www.arttoday.com*.

Some images used in this publication are copyright *Corel Corporation*.

Some images used in this publication are copyright *National Aeronautics and Space Administration*.

An image used on page 148 herein was obtained from *IMSI's Master Photos Collection*, 1895 Francisco Blvd. East, San Rafael CA. 94901-5506, USA

Some images in this document are from www.clipart.com, copyright (c) 2011 Jupiterimages Corporation.

The images used in this publication may not be reproduced in whole or in part without the permission of the copyright holder.

ORDERING INFORMATION

SCHOOL ORDERS

Please contact the Learning Resource Centre (LRC) for school discount and order information.

THE KEY **Study Guides** are specifically designed to assist students in preparing for unit tests, final exams, and provincial examinations.

THE KEY **Study Guides**—$29.95 each plus G.S.T.

SENIOR HIGH		JUNIOR HIGH	ELEMENTARY
Biology 30	Biology 20	English Language Arts 9	English Language Arts 6
Chemistry 30	Chemistry 20	Mathematics 9	Mathematics 6
English 30-1	English 20-1	Science 9	Science 6
English 30-2	Mathematics 20-1	Social Studies 9	Social Studies 6
Mathematics 30-1	Physics 20	Mathematics 8	Mathematics 4
Mathematics 30-2	Social Studies 20-1	Mathematics 7	English Language Arts 3
Physics 30	English 10-1		Mathematics 3
Social Studies 30-1	Mathematics 10		
Social Studies 30-2	Combined		
	Science 10		
	Social Studies 10-1		

Student Notes and Problems (SNAP) Workbooks contain complete explanations of curriculum concepts, examples, and exercise questions.

SNAP Workbooks—$29.95 each plus G.S.T.

SENIOR HIGH		JUNIOR HIGH	ELEMENTARY
Biology 30	Biology 20	Mathematics 9	Mathematics 6
Chemistry 30	Chemistry 20	Science 9	Mathematics 5
Mathematics 30-1	Mathematics 20-1	Mathematics 8	Mathematics 4
Mathematics 30-2	Physics 20	Science 8	Mathematics 3
Mathematics 31	Mathematics 10	Mathematics 7	
Physics 30	Combined	Science 7	
	Science 10		

Class Notes and Problem Solved—$19.95 each plus G.S.T.

SENIOR HIGH		JUNIOR HIGH
Biology 30	Biology 20	Mathematics 9
Chemistry 30	Chemistry 20	Science 9
Mathematics 30-1	Mathematics 20-1	Mathematics 8
Mathematics 30-2	Physics 20	Science 8
Mathematics 31	Mathematics 10 Combined	Mathematics 7
Physics 30	Science 10	Science 7

Visit our website for a tour of resource content and features or order resources online at
www.castlerockresearch.com/store/

#2340, 10180 – 101 Street NW
Edmonton, AB Canada T5J 3S4
e-mail: learn@castlerockresearch.com

Phone: 780.448.9619
Toll-free: 1.800.840.6224
Fax: 780.426.3917

ORDER FORM

THE KEY	QUANTITY
Biology 30	
Chemistry 30	
English 30-1	
English 30-2	
Mathematics 30-1	
Mathematics 30-2	
Physics 30	
Social Studies 30-1	
Social Studies 30-2	
Biology 20	
Chemistry 20	
English 20-1	
Mathematics 20-1	
Physics 20	
Social Studies 20-1	
English 10-1	
Math 10 Combined	
Science 10	
Social Studies 10-1	
Social Studies 9	
English Language Arts 9	
Mathematics 9	
Science 9	
Mathematics 8	
Mathematics 7	
English Language Arts 6	
Mathematics 6	
Science 6	
Social Studies 6	
Mathematics 4	
Mathematics 3	
English Language Arts 3	

Student Notes and Problems Workbooks	QUANTITY	
	SNAP Workbooks	Solution Manuals
Mathematics 31		
Biology 30		
Chemistry 30		
Mathematics 30-1		
Mathematics 30-2		
Physics 30		
Biology 20		
Chemistry 20		
Mathematics 20-1		
Physics 20		
Mathematics 10 Combined		
Science 10		
Mathematics 9		
Science 9		
Mathematics 8		
Science 8		
Mathematics 7		
Science 7		
Mathematics 6		
Mathematics 5		
Mathematics 4		
Mathematics 3		

Problem Solved and Class Notes	QUANTITY	
	Class Notes	Problem Solved
Mathematics 31		
Biology 30		
Chemistry 30		
Mathematics 30-1		
Mathematics 30-2		
Physics 30		
Biology 20		
Chemistry 20		
Mathematics 20-1		
Physics 20		
Mathematics 10 Combined		
Science 10		
Mathematics 9		
Science 9		
Mathematics 8		
Science 8		
Mathematics 7		
Science 7		

Total Cost

Subtotal 1	
Subtotal 2	
Subtotal 3	
Cost Subtotal	
Shipping and Handling*	
G.S.T	
Order Total	

Learning Resources Centre

Castle Rock Research is pleased to participate in an exclusive distribution arrangement with the Learning Resources Centre (LRC). Under this agreement, schools can place all their orders with LRC for order fulfillment. As well, these resources are eligible for applying the Learning Resource Credit Allocation (LRCA), which gives schools a 25% discount off LRC's selling price. Call LRC for details.

Orders may be placed with LRC by
Telephone: 780.427.2767
Fax: 780.422.9750
Internet: www.lrc.education.gov.ab.ca
Or mail: 12360 – 142 Street NW
Edmonton, AB T5L 4X9

PAYMENT AND SHIPPING INFORMATION

Name: _____
School _____
Telephone: _____
SHIP TO
School: _____
Address: _____
City: _____ Postal Code: ____
PAYMENT
☐ By credit card   VISA/MC
Number: _____
Expiry Date: _____
Name on card: _____
☐ Enclosed cheque
☐ Invoice school   P.O. number: ____

*(Please call for current rates)

■ ■ ■
CASTLE ROCK RESEARCH CORP   #2340, 10180 – 101 Street NW, Edmonton, AB T5J 3S4   **Phone:** 780.448.9619 **Fax:** 780.426.3917
Email: learn@castlerockresearch.com   **Toll-free:** 1.800.840.6224
www.castlerockresearch.com